The New York Times
Great Songs of the Yiddish Theater

A Note on Transliteration

The reader will find that the transliteration from the Yiddish to English text differs in some ways from traditional American usage. In this book we have used a new and modernized standardization of transliteration established by the YIVO Institute for Jewish Research to overcome the problem of dialectal differences among Jews coming from different parts of the Old World. For example, the familiar gutteral sound in what used to be transliterated as "ich," is now spelled "ikh." The key to pronunciation, as used in this book, follows:

AY	as in MINE	U	as in LOOK
A	as in FATHER	EY	as in OBEY
KH	as in BACH	E	as in NET
O	as in MORE	I	as in BIT

Arranged for
Voice, Piano, and Guitar
(lyrics transliterated)
Selected by
Norman H. Warembud
Foreword by Molly Picon

NYT Quadrangle/The New York Times Book Co.

Photo captions

page 53 (clockwise from upper right); Scene from "Der Litvisher Yankee," with Jack Rechtzeit, Bella Finkel, Sidney Hart, Aaron Lebedeff, Bertha Hart, Abe Sincoff, and ensemble; Molly Picon as a child actress; Irving Jacobson and Mae Schonfeld; Molly Picon in the seder scene from "Yankele"; Herman Yablokoff as "The Clown"; Leo Fuchs; Ludwig Satz. *Center:* Sheet music cover, "Das Lebedige Yisoimele."

page 119 (clockwise from upper right): Scene from "Der Eybiker Vanderer," with Charles Nathanson, Jacob Ben-Ami, Celia Adler, Bina Abramowitz, Maurice Schwartz, Lazar Fried, and Rebecca Weintraub; Celia Adler and Maurice Schwartz; David Kessler, Jennie Goldstein, and Malvina Lobel in "Dos Yidish Hartz"; Sigmund Mogulesko; Khayim Tauber, Miriam Kressyn, and Seymour Rechtzeit; Samuel Goldenburg; Aaron Lebedeff and Leon Blank in "Der Groiser Nes"; Jennie Goldstein as "Di Froy Fun Der Velt." *Center:* Abraham Goldfadden.

page 149 (clockwise from upper right): Leon Blank and Anna Teitelbaum Skulnick; Mischa Gehrman, Max Rosenblatt, and Lucy Gehrman; Meeting of Jewish Composers Society: Alexander Olshanetsky, Abraham Ellstein, Joseph Brody, Joseph Steinberg (attorney), Joseph Rumshinsky, Harry Lubin, A. E. Markowitz (attorney), and Sholom Secunda; Yetta Zwerling and Jacob Jacobs; Aaron Lebedeff and Lucy Levine. *Center:* Menashe Skulnick.

Library of Congress Catalog Card Number: 75-8285
International Standard Book Number: 0-8129-0574-1

Selections supervised by Norman H. Warembud
Transliteration and music editing by Zalmen Mlotek
Music autography by Music Art Co.
Design by Libra Graphics, Inc.
Photos courtesy of the Friends of the Theater and Music Collection, The Museum of the City of New York, and the Yiddish Theatrical Alliance.

CONTENTS

Foreword

by Molly Picon

It warms my heart to see that the centennial of the Yiddish theater is being marked by the issuance of *Great Songs of the Yiddish Theater*. This collection of musical memories brings to mind the rich outpouring of songs that added such an important dimension to our lives.

Our celebration commemorates one hundred years of Yiddish theater as this generation knows it. But, actually, the beginning of Yiddish theater itself dates back to a movement in the middle of the eighteenth century, the so-called Jewish Enlightenment, led by Moses Mendelssohn (1729–1786). This movement set out to disparage Yiddish as a jargon of the streets, unworthy to be a literary language. Though at first this had a detrimental effect, it finally unified the proponents of Yiddish and inspired a determined effort to make it the true Jewish folk language.

The first dramatic representations of this period were drawn from the stories closest to home, representing, for example, the *Purimshpil*, the heroic Purim festival story of Queen Esther's victory over Haman and a classic symbol of Jewish faith despite oppression. There were the Old Testament events of *Abraham and Isaac*, *Naomi and Ruth*, and *Joseph and His Brothers*, all of which were superb vehicles for portrayal in the folk language.

During the latter part of the eighteenth century, Mendel Levin (1749–1846) made the first chink in the armor when he broke away from the Jewish Enlightenment by publishing biblical passages in Yiddish. Soon after, there appeared numerous works in Yiddish. With stories and plays by Yisroel Aksenfeld (1787–1866) and fables and plays by Solomon Ettinger (1800–1856), Yiddish was on its way! A complete Yiddish play written by Isaac Abraham Euchel (1758–1804), a one-time collaborator of Mendelssohn, in itself represented a tremendous victory for the *Yiddishists* and led to the full acceptance of Yiddish as a literary and dramatic language.

In the second half of the nineteenth century, Yiddish literature and drama entered what can be termed as its "golden age" of creativity. Such outstanding literary figures as Mendele Mokher Sforim (S. Y. Abramovitch, 1836–1917), Yitskhok Leyb Peretz (1851–1915), and Sholom Aleykhem (Solomon Rabinowitz, 1859–1916), to name only three, brought literary distinction to this young language in form and style, satire, humor, characterization, the sensitive and aesthetic use of idiomatic expression.

In this period, Avrom Goldfaden (1840–1908), often referred to as the father of the Yiddish musical theater, opened the first showplace in Jassy, Rumania, where he presented his epochal works, including *Bar Kokhba*, *Ahkaydes Yitskhok*, and *Shulamis*. Goldfaden was a giant of creativity. A poet, playwright, composer, actor, and director, he served the Yiddish theater well and left many musical memories, one of which, "Rozhinkes mit Mandl'n," is included in this volume.

Many other theatrical groups and personalities sprang up around Goldfaden's theater. Nurtured there, they grew and went off to tour from city to city, bringing with them the Yiddish word and song wherever they went. The Brodersons, the Tomashevskys, the Adlers, and the Kesslers are some of the antecedents of the families of the Yiddish theater of today. As the nineteenth century drew to a close, the Yiddish theater was ready to move to *dos goldene land*—America.

Just as Yiddish literature and Yiddish journalism centered on East Broadway, New York, the Yiddish theater almost immediately took up residence on Second Avenue, which soon could hardly house the number of theaters that were required to meet the appetite of the immigrant population. The theater brought to life their dreams, their difficulties in the new world, and the nostalgia for their old homes, the *shtetl* from which they came.

The American–Yiddish playwrights were especially adept at devising vehicles that drew an emotional response from the spectator. By artful use of the specialties of their performers, they fashioned a large and loyal audience. Their followers soon outgrew the confines of Second Avenue and demanded and supported Yiddish theaters all over New York and, as the population moved, all over America. In the late twenties it was not unusual for more than a dozen companies to be holding forth in New York, with new productions ranging in theatrical fare from full-blown opera, historical, classical, and contemporary drama to operetta and musical comedy. The Yiddish Art Theater specialized in literary drama, and the Folks Theater offered repertory. Meanwhile, Yiddish theater continued to grow throughout Europe, particularly in Russia, Poland, Lithuania, Austria, Germany, and France.

To the musical theater were attracted a retinue of composers and lyricists whose compositions were not counted by tens, or even by hundreds, but by thousands. The talents of composers such as Peretz Sandler, Herman Wohl, Louis Gilrod, Albert Perlmutter, Adolph King, David Meyerowitz, and, more recently, giants such as Joseph Rumshinsky, Sholom Secunda, Alexander Olshanetsky, Abraham Ellstein, Illya Trilling, Yasha Kreitzberg, and others have enriched our lives. I would be remiss if I didn't include some of my colleagues—the lyricists, to whom naturally I am very partial. These are writers like Anshel Schorr, Isadore Lillian, Morris Rund, and Nuchum Stutchkoff, and, more recently, Jacob Jacobs, Khayim Tauber, Israel Rosenberg, and the outstanding Yiddish poets who contributed vital literary texts and ideas—Itzik Manger, Mani Lieb, Avrohom Reisen, Aaron Tzeitlin, Khayim Nachman Bialik, Nakhum Yud, Wolf Younin, and many others.

The death knell for the Yiddish theater throughout the world sounded when Hitler came to power in Germany, when occupation and anti-Semitism spread through Europe. Shortly before, the United States had put an end to immigration. As second-generation, assimilated Jews replaced their parents, devotion and dedication unhappily declined. Theaters began to close. The depression pushed this along; without food on the table, who could think of theater?

As emigrants from Europe forsook the United States in favor of Central and South America, the theater followed this potential audience. Many American performers joined their European counterparts driven from Europe by Hitler. But these small Jewish communities separated by large distances did not provide the concentration of talent and interest that had existed a quarter-century before in New York.

Other Yiddish theater folk abandoned the profession in favor of more lucrative and rewarding activity in American theater, motion pictures, radio, and television, yet leaving behind a core of dedicated personalities and an audience who just never gives up. To this day, year after year, there are new productions and revivals.

Recently, I went to the Yiddish theater to see *Hard to Be a Jew* and frankly was surprised to see a line stretching around the corner, buying tickets at the box office. As I approached the entrance, I overheard one woman say to another, "I've been waiting here for half an hour and the line doesn't seem to move. No wonder the Yiddish theater is dying—you just can't get tickets!"

Molly Picon

ABI GEZUNT

A tremendous hit from the film, "Mamele" where she introduced it, this became Molly Picon's theme song.
The air is free, the sun shines for rich and poor alike.
As long as you're healthy you're happy.

Lyrics by MOLLY PICON Music by ABRAHAM ELLSTEIN

B7 Em Am6 Am Em
A shukh, a zok, a kleyd on la - tes, in ke - she - ne a
A Em C F♯ B7 Em
dray, fir zlo - tes, A - bi ge - zunt, ken men glik - lekh zayn.
3 3
Am Em
Di luft is fray far ye - dn glaykh
3 3
Am Am6 B Am
Di zun zi shaynt far ye - dn ey - nem o - rem o - der raykh

A B Em Am6 Am Em
A bi - sl freyd, a bi - sl la - khn, a mol mit fraynt a
sff
A Em C F# B7 1.Em B7
shnep - sl ma - khn, A - bi ge - zunt ken men glik - lekh zayn. A
2.Em Fine
Verse:
Em Am6
zayn.
Ey-ner zukht a-shi - res, Ey-ner zukht ge vi - res,
B7 Em B B7 Em
Ay-nem-en di gan - tse velt. Ey - ner meynt dos gan - tse glik

F♯7 B Em
hengt nor op in gelt, Zo - ln a - le zu - khn,
Am6 B7 Em
zo - ln a - le kri - khn, nor ikh trakht bay mir, Ikh
F♯ F♯7 B C♯m F♯6 B B7
rit.
D. S. al Fine
darf dos oyf ka - po - res vayl dos glik-shteyt ba mayn tir. A
rit.
sff

AY-AY-AY

A khasidic composition featured in the production "Fishel der Gerutener" which starred Menashe Skulnick at the Yiddish Folks Theatre in New York. It was sung in the show by Fania Rubina.
Forget your enemies, just sing and rejoice
The Messiah will come and we will praise him.

Words by ISRAEL ROSENBERG Music by JOSEPH RUMSHINSKY

E
zey.
f
Ay, Ay, Ay, Ay, Ay, Ay,
f
Am6
E7
Dm7
B7
E
ev - du a - doy shem be - sim - kho frey - zikh khotch - es tut dir vey— Ay, Ay, Ay,
E
Dm
E
Ay, Ay, Ay, hos - tu so - nim zay me - va - tl zey.
Am
Oy ku - men vet mo - shi - akh - bim hey - ro

F
un zin-gen ve-ln a-le bim hey-ro oy be-yo-mey-nu
F
oy oy oy oy be-doy-rey-nu
mp E
Ay, Ay, Ay,
mp
Ay, Ay, Ay,
E
Am6
ev-du a-doy shem be-sim-kho
E7
Dm7
B7
frey zikh khotch-es tut dir vey
E
Ay, Ay, Ay, Ay, Ay, Ay,

Dm
E
f
hos - tu so - nim zay me - va - tl zey.
Ay, Ay, Ay,
f
E
Am6
Ay, Ay, Ay, ev - du a - doy shem be - sim - kho
E7
Dm
B7
E
frey zikh khotch - es tut dir vey
Ay, Ay, Ay,
E
rall.
Dm
E
Ay, Ay, Ay, hos - tu so - nim zay me - va - tl zey.
rall.

AZOY IZ GEVEN, AZOY VET ES ZAYN

Leon Liebgold sang this to Molly Picon in one of the last musicals to play the Second Avenue Theatre in New York.

Since the begining of time we were destined for each other.
As in Biblical days I am committed to you.
That's how it was then, and ever shall be.

Words by MOLLY PICON Music by JOSEPH RUMSHINSKY

Valse tempo
Gm Bb Cm D7 Gm
f
Gm D7 Gm
Oyb s'iz ba - shert dir a zi - vig, men zogt, Vert dort far -
D D7
shri - bn ge - noy, Du megst zikh var - fn, tsum

Gm
Eb
Gm
D7
sof ves - tu dar - fn zayn may - ne, vayl es shteyt a - zoy,
Gm
D7
Gm
Nokh fun be - rey-shis es firt zikh, you see, Az ven an
Cm
D7
er treft a zi, Zogt zi fri - er neyn, es vet

A7
D
keyn mol ge - shen, Shpe-ter o - ber der - nokh git zi tsi.
rit.
Chorus:
Gm
Cm
Oy, a - zoy is ge - ven, oy,
D7
Gm
G
a - zoy vet es zayn, Oy, s'vet
Bdim
Cm
F7
B♭
to - mid ge - shen, Vi lang di velt vet nor shteyn.

B♭6
Cm
Koym zet a bo - kher a mey - dl un bald,
Gm
Cm
D7
Gm
Hoybt on tsu tyokh - ken zayn harts a ge - vald. Oy,
Cm
Gm6
D7
a - zoy iz ge - ven, Oy, a - zoy vet es
1.
Gm
2.
Gm
D7
Gm
zayn.
zayn.

A BIS'L LIBE, UN A BISELE GLIK

One of Molly Picon's early starring vehicles at the Second Avenue Theatre was "Tzirkus Meyd'l" for which she collaborated on this important song.
Just a little love, some good fortune.
If only the sun would shine for a moment
and bring some good luck to me.

Lyric by MOLLY PICON   Music by JOSEPH RUMSHINSKY

Gb Abm7 Db Edim Fdim
bin in der velt a - roys. Ge - zen vi men - tchn zey
Gbdim B7 Am6 Gbdim Bb7
zay - nen far shtelt, Ge - vo - rn iz mir fin - tster mayn velt.
Chorus: Moderate Tempo
Eb6 Eb Bb7
A bi - sl li - be un a bis - el - e glik,
Fm6 Bb7 Eb
Di zun zol shay - nen nor oyf eyn oy - gn - blik

Eb6 Eb Bb7 Cm Gm Ab Eb
Ven ikh zol ke - nen in mayn
Bb7 Bb7 Bbaug
hartz a - rayn Bren - gen zu - nen shayn oyf eyn mi -
Eb D7 Eb6 Bb7
nit A bi - sl li - be un a bis - el - e glik
Bb7 Fm6 Bb7 Eb
Di zun zol shay - nen nor oyf eyn oy - gn - blik

C
C7
Fm
Fm6
Cm
B♭7
Der li - ber Got hot ye - dn ge - ge - bn
E♭
Gm
A♭
Fm
B♭7
A zoy fil glik in le - bn nor mir keyn zakh
1.
E♭
D7
2.
E♭
nit.
A bi - sl nit.

A BRIVELE DER MAM'N

Originally a poem by the noted folk-poet, he set it to music and it flourished in the vaudeville theatres after World War I at the height of Jewish immigration.
Don't neglect to write your mother.
Your letter is all she has to keep you close to her and heal her broken heart.

Words and Music by SOLOMON SHMULOWITZ

Adim Gm A7 D7 Gm
bet mit tre - rn un mit shrek dayn tray - e
kin - dersh harts iz hart vi shteyn kayn eyn - tsik
voynt ir kind er lebt gor groys a glik - le -

Cm D7 Gm Bb
li - be mu - ter du forst mayn kind, mayn
briv ba - ku - men vi ken mayn kind, gor
khe fa - mil - ye. A shey - ne froi un

G7 Cm G7 Cm
eyn - tsik kind a - ri - ber vay - te ya - men
ho - bn mut vi geyt im ayn dos le - bn
kin - der tsvey mit likh - ti - ke ge - shtal - tn

D7 Gm E♭
Akh kum a hin nor frish ge - zunt un
Es muz im geyn dort zey - er gut vayl
Un vi er zitst un kvelt fun zey hot

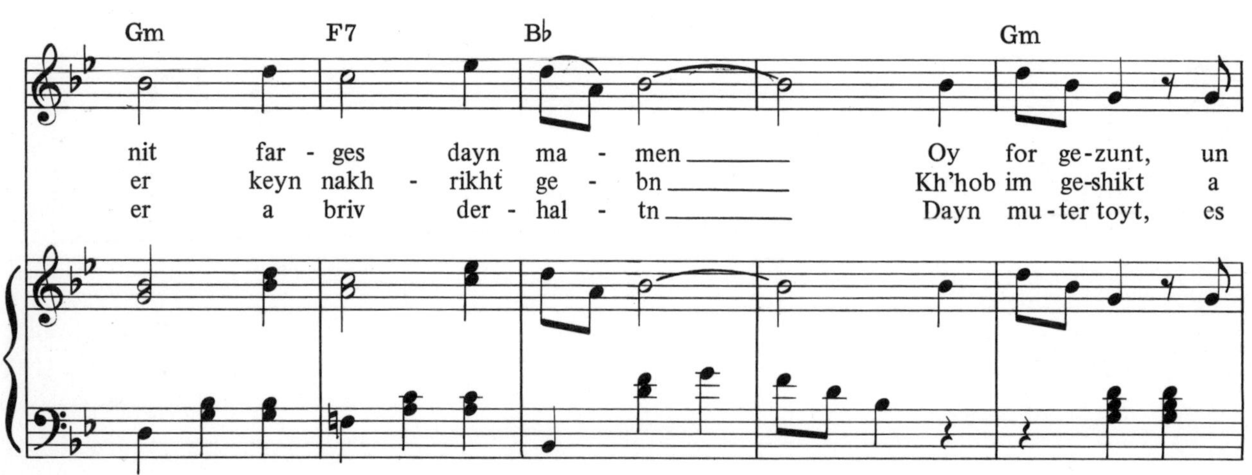
Gm F7 B♭ Gm
nit far - ges dayn ma - men Oy for ge-zunt, un
er keyn nakh - rikht ge - bn Kh'hob im ge-shikt a
er a briv der - hal - tn Dayn mu-ter toyt, es

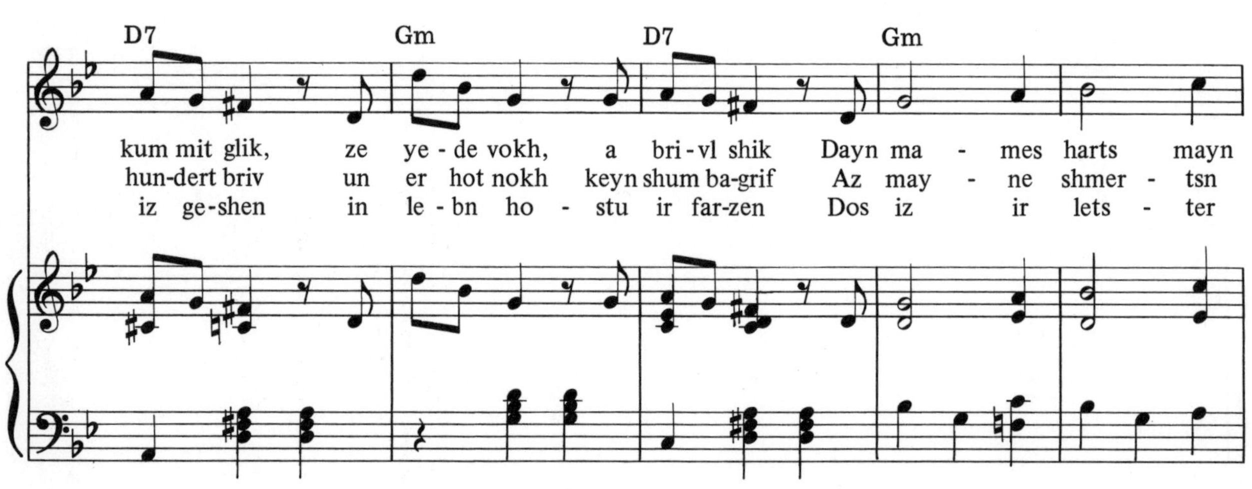
D7 Gm D7 Gm
kum mit glik, ze ye - de vokh, a bri - vl shik Dayn ma - mes harts mayn
hun-dert briv un er hot nokh keyn shum ba-grif Az may - ne shmer - tsn
iz ge-shen in le - bn ho - stu ir far-zen Dos iz ir lets - ter

Andante moderato
Gm C6 D Chorus: Gm D7 Gm D7
kind der - kvik.
ze - nen tif. A 1. & 2. bri - ve - le der mam-en zol - stu - nit far-
vuntch ge - ven. 3. ka - di - shl der mam-en zol - stu - nit far-
Gm B♭ Cm E♭6 F7 B♭
za - men Shrayb ge-shvind li - bes kind shenk ir di ne - kho-me, Di
za - men Zog ge-shvind li - bes kind shenk ir di ne - kho-me, Di
Gm D7 Gm B♭ Gm B♭ Cm6
ma-me vet dayn bri - ve - le lezn un zi vert ge - ne - zn Heylst ir shmerts
ma-me vet ir ka - dish e - rn in ir key - ver ge - rn Heylst ir shmerts
Gdim E♭ E♭6 D7 1. Gm 2. Cm6 Gm
ir bi - ter hartz der - kvikst ir di ne - sho - me. A
ir bi - ter hartz der - kvikst ir di ne - sho - me.

DAYNE

"Maz'l-tov, Molly," H. Kalmanovich's musical starred Molly Picon at the Second Avenue Theatre and provided this charmer.
Yours, I remain forever, to bring you only joy and happiness. The whole world is mine because I am yours.

Lyric by MOLLY PICON Music by JOSEPH RUMSHINSKY

Gm
A7
D7
Gm
zayn, to-mid mir a - leyn.
Chorus:
Gm
D7
Day - ne,
ikh vel far-blay - bn nor day - ne.
Gm
A
Cm6
Ikh vel far-tray - bn di zorg un di lay - dn, bren - gen nor freyd un
A7
D
Gm
glik far undz bey - dn, nor.
Day - ne,

D7
ven ikh vel ve - rn nor day - ne. Dan vet oyf-he - rn mayn
Gm Cm Cm6 D Gm
vey - tik un payn, kh'vel ey - bik nor day - ne zayn.
D7 Gm Dm G7
Li - bn dikh a - leyn, un
Cm Gm D7 Gm A7 Dm
tray vel ikh dir zayn, keyn mol ba - tri - gn dikh, mayn

C Cm6 Gm D7 Gm
ke - ni - gn, ves - tu zayn, lyu - be, may - ne, may - ne.
D7
Di gan - tse velt vet zayn may - ne. Di zun vet far mir oyf -
Gm Cm6 D7 1 Gm
shay - nen, ven ikh vel day - ne, nor day - ne zayn.
D7 2. Gm D7 Gm
zayn.

Der Alter Tzigayner

A production number which was featured in the musical, "Bublitshki," in which Molly Picon appeared at the Public Theatre in New York.
Listen to the strains of the old gypsy's fiddle. Its haunting melody will touch your soul, excite your emotions, and make you feel great to be alive.

Lyric by JACOB JACOBS Music by ABRAHAM ELLSTEIN

Andante
Fm 6
sff
Fm
Fm
p
Dort oyf a ber - ge - le un - ter dem fray - en hi - ml,
tr
Fm
Bb m
Vayt fun dem ra - shi - kn shtots ge - ri - ml

Db7
Fm
Db7
Shteyt zikh a khat-ke-le a-leyn oyf an ort An al-ter tsi-gay-ner voynt dort.
f
Fm
Fm
ff
Dort he-rn zikh te-ner zeyer
f
Bbm6
Bbm
zi-se vos vey-nen in mi-nor
Ven oyf zayn fi-dl far-
rit.
Fm
Db7
geyt zikh der al-ter tsi-gay-ner
Mit zayn gan-tsn fay-er un

Fm
Db7
Fm
bren
Nor vi a tsi-gay-ner ken. A
pp
Allegro
F
F6
Chorus:
f
A tsi-gay-ner me-lo
Ven ir hert es dakht zikh
di iz a-zoy sheyn
aykh s'iz prost na-iv,
Hert ir es, far-gest ir es nit
Un ir hot dan gor nit kayn ba-
F7
neyn
grif
Vayl zi iz va-rem, har-tsik, ful mit kheyn
Vi es rirt on di ne-sho-me tif.

B♭m
A mod-ne kraft
Fun ye-de tsayt
F
Zi git aykh li-be un oykh lay-dn-shaft
Zi filt aykh on mit lust un frey-lekh-kayt.
Hert ir es
On-hal-tn
C7
nor eyn mol git es keyn ru
vilt ir ey-bik ot a-di
S'far ki-sheft aykh di me-lo-
Di klan-gen fun di me-lo-
F
1. C F6 C
2. F F7 B♭m F7
di.
di.
Ven

Allegro
B♭m
der tsi-gay-ner shpilt tsu - zayn li - dl, In
C7
F7
harts git a bri Fun zayn fi - dl
F7
B♭m
der klang Der vekt dayn ne - sho-mes far - lang
B♭m
Dayn blut es kokht un es zit, Zayn

B♭m
B♭m7
E♭m
fi - dl dem boy - gn er tsit.
Nemt in di him-len shve - bn,
B♭m
F7
1.
B♭m
Es glust zikh nor tsum le - bn,
Dos le - bn vert dan a - zoy git.
2.
B♭m
Cm
B♭m
git.
A
A
F7
B♭m
Dos iz dem al - tn tsi - gay - ners lid.

DER NAYER SHER

Written in a car, between concerts, for a recording session with Seymour Rechtzeit on RCA-Victor, this became a favorite of all the record artists. Its name, in English, is "The Wedding Samba." Edmundo Ross gave it its world debut.

Now musicians, it's time to play the new tune.
Everyone dance!
No more worries, only joy as we dance this new two-step.

Words and Music by ABRAHAM ELLSTEIN

Lively
F
ff
Chorus:
F
F7
Hey,_ du klez - mer, nem_ dem fi - dl, shpil dos nay - e li - dl,
p
F6
C7
F
C7
tan - tsn vet men dem na - yem sher.

F
F7
In a ka - ra - hod men dreyt zikh, un dos harts der - freyt zikh,
F6
C7
F
nor ven men tanst dem nay - em sher.
ff
F
F7
He - kher, he - kher biz di stel - ye, shpringt der zey - de, El - ye,
F6
C7
F
es vilt zikh le - bn im vos mer.
Un di

F
F7
bo - be, Sos - ye kvelt fun na - khes, so - nim oyf tsu la - khes.
F6
C7
F
F7
Tan - tsn vet men dem nay - em sher. Nu zet, nor
B♭m
B♭m6
F
zet vi ye - der freyt zikh un vi men
C
C6
C7
F
F7
dreyt zikh un men tu - pet mit di - fis. Dos harts tse -

Bb
Bb6
F
F6
geyt nor tan-tsn bet zikh vayl ven men
Gm
F
C7
To Coda
F
tantst vert dan dos le-bn a-zoy zis.
f
Verse:
F
Bbm6
F
Frey-lekh zayn a-tsind dar-fn mir a-le troy-rik zayn dos
Toy-gn a-le day-ges a-le zor-gn oy-fn har-tsn
G7
C
C7
vet men shoyn nisht mer. Vayl ba-ze-tsn vet men bald di
ven es iz dir shver. Be-ser, bru-der, ho-fn az biz

C7
F
Dm
C7
ka - le
un tan - tsn vet men gor dem nay - em
mor - gn
veln a - le in ey - nem tan - tsn dem nay - em
1. F
2. F
C7
D. C. to Chorus
sher.
Vos
sher.
ff
Coda
F
F7
zis
Ah.
ff
F
C7
F

DI GRINEH KUZINE

The most famous song of its time, it was featured across the country and throughout the world in cafés and theaters after its debut at the Grand St. Theatre in New York.
My country cousin is something special, with her beautiful eyes and rosy cheeks. Her feet beg to dance. She's outstanding!

Words by HYMAN PRIZANT   Music by ABE SCHWARTZ

Moderate tempo
Intro:
Gm
D7
Gm
D7
ff
Voice:
Gm
Tsu mir iz ge - kum - en a ku - zi - ne,
Her - re - lekh gol - de - ne ge - lok - te,
mf
Dm
A7
D7
Sheyn vi gold iz zi ge - ven di gri - ne,
Tsayn - de - lekh vi pe - re - lekh ge - tok - te,

D7 Gm C Cm
Be - ke - lekh vi roy - te po - me - ran - tsn,
Ey - ge lekh vi tay - be - lekh a tsvi - ling,
Gm A D7 Gm D Gm Cm6
Fi - se - lekh vos be - tn zikh tsum tan - tsn.
Li - pe - lekh vi kar - she lekh in fri - ling;
D7 Gm C Cm
Be - ke - lekh vi roy - te po - me - ran - tsn,
Ey - ge - lekh vi tay - be - lekh a tsvi - ling;
Gm A D7 Gm D7 Gm
Fi - se - lekh vos be - tn zikh tsum tan - tsn.
Li - pe - lekh vi kar - she - lekh in fri - ling.
Fine
(For finish of song only)

Interlude: Faster
Gm
D7
Gm D7
Gm
D. S.
ff
a tempo
Dance (A la Freylekh)
Gm
ff
Gm
Gm
D7
1.
Gm
2.
Gm
D7
Gm

DOS PINTELE YID

The title song of Boris Tomashefsky's first great musical hit which opened at the National Theatre in New York. The production has continued to play throughout the world, until this very day.
Despite rejection and persecution, despite suffering and torture, the Jew's courage is his greatness and perseverance.

Words by LOUIS GILROD Music by ARNOLD PERLMUTTER/HERMAN WOHL

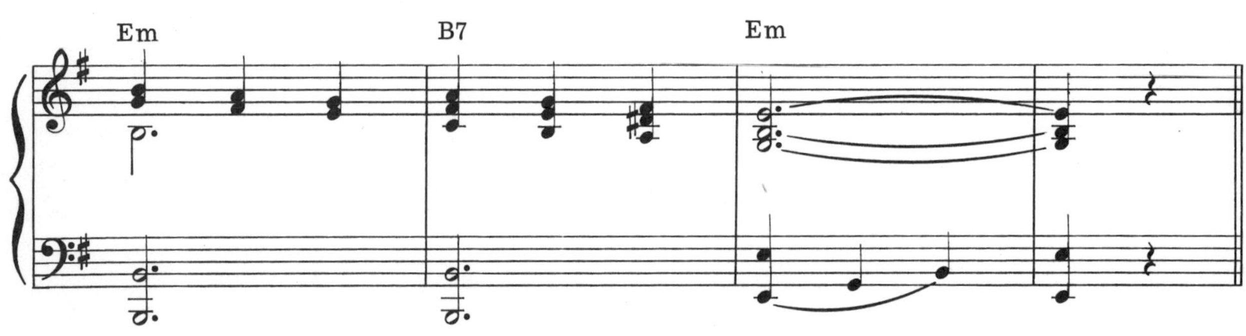

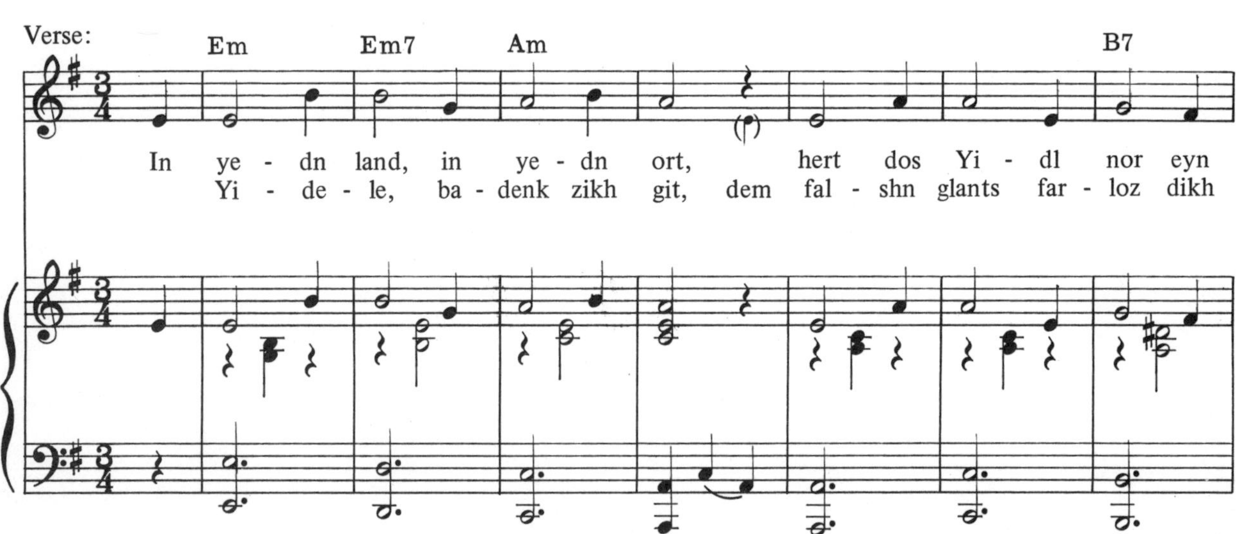

Em B7 Em Am
vort: a Yid bis - tu, gey dir, mir dar - fn dikh nit, a frem - der
nit, Zo - gar ven es treft zikh dir shoyn a land, vos git dir
D7 G B7 Em Em7 Am
bis - tu, a ger. Dos Yi - dl van - dert un vert nit
glay - khe rekht. Du han - dlst mit a fray - er
D7 G D7 G
mid, trogt in har - tsn dos pin - te - le Yid, er lakht fun di
hant, dayn klu - ger moy - akh makht raykh dos land, oykh dort muz - stu
Am B7 Em
so - nim ven Got iz mit im. Ver ken im shlekhts - ton, ver?
lay - dn vayl du bist a Yid. Men dankt dir op zey - er shlekht

D7 G
Fil mol iz ge - bro - khn Yis - ro - liks ge - mit, er beygt zikh far
Da - rum folg mikh, yi - de - le, ge - nug noyt un shand, nokh tsi - on blozt
D7 G B7 E
dem klen - stn vin - te - le. Dokh der gres - ter shtu - rem oys -
yetst dir a vin - te - le. Un ruf day - ne bri - der - lekh in
Am E7 Am D7 B7 Em
vorts - len ken nit dos shey - nin - ke, kley - nin - ke pin - te - le.
dayn ey - gn land, vayl dort iz di heym fun dem pin - te - le.
Em Am Em Am
Dos pin - te - le yid iz zey - er git, ko - vid un shtolts

Tempo I
rall.
Em
Em
C
B7
ma - kht es dir, Yid.
Akht es, un shets es, un hit:
rall.
Moderate Tempo
Chorus:
Em
Yi - de - le, dayn kroyn iz dos pin - te - le Yid,
Em
Fil ge - li - tn shoyn far dem pin - te - le Yid, Ge -
D7
G
B7
Em
ma - tert day - ne gli - der - lekh, ge - pay - nikt day - ne bri - der - lekh, ge -

G D7 G D7 G
bo - dn zikh hot ye - der in dayn blit. Bil - bu - lim on a tsol oyf dem
G D
pin - te - le Yid. Dokh mu - tik a - le mol blaybt dos pin - te - le Yid. Der
G7 D7 B7 Em
klu - gitsh - ker Yis - ro - li - kl lakht fun dir, a - mo - li - kl, un
C6 B7 1. Em B7 2. Em
blaybt tray dem pin - te - le yid. yid.

DAS LEBEDIGE YISOIMELE
THE ORPHAN GIRL
DRAMATIC SONG FROM THE PLAY
BLIND LOVE
דאס לעבעדיגע יתומהלע
פון ז. ליבינס דראמא
בלינדע ליעבע
WORDS BY MR. BORIS THOMASHEFSKY
MUSIC BY PERLMUTTER & WOHL
Featured in
Z. LIBIN'S DRAMA
As Produced at Thomashefsky's "PEOPLES THEATRE"
Published by
A. TERES
MUSIC DEALER AND PUBLISHER
88 DELANCEY ST. N.Y.

DU BIST DOS LIKHT FUN MAYNE OYG'N

Introduced at the Second Avenue Theatre production of Louis Freiman's musical comedy, "Yosel, Un Zayne Vayber" which starred Menashe Skulnick.
You are the sparkle of my eyes, the zest of my life. You brighten the world for me.

Words by ISADORE LILLIAN Music by JOSEPH RUMSHINSKY

Gm
Cm
Gm
F
le - bn mir,
Git mayn harts a pik,
Du host mayn harts ge -
C
C♯dim
Dm
ge - bn mir,
Nem es nit tsu - rik.
Le - bn ken ikh
Gm
Dm
nit on dir,
Zol - tsu vi - sn zayn;
Vey - stu vos du
Gm
Gdim
A
meynst tsu mir,
Yo - sl, her zikh ayn:
Du bist dos

A
B7
A7
Dm
likht fun may - ne oy gn Nor du ba -
D
E7
D7
Gm
C
shaynst mayn velt far mir Du host mikh
A
Dm
B♭
C7
tsu zikh tsu - ge - tsoy - gn Az le - bn
F
C7
F
A7
ken ikh nit on dir. Du makhst mayn

A
B7
A7
Dm
nakht zol likh - tik ve - rn, Dem bloy - en
D
E7
D7
Gm
C
hi ml breng - stu mir, Du bist mayn
A
Dm
B♭
C7
F
he - ler mor - gn - shte - rn Nu shayn far mir
A7
Dm
F
ikh bet bay dir Bis - tu nit le - bn mir Iz mir

F7 D7 Gm G♯dim E7
khoy - shekh fints - ter, tun - kl, Un der - her ikh dayn shtim Vert tog
A A B♭ G A7
in a - ye - dn vin - kl. Du bist dos likht fun may - ne
Dm B♭ A
1.
oy - gn Nor du ba - shaynst mayn velt far
Dm A
2.
A7 Dm
mir. Du bist dos mayn velt far mir.

DU FEHLST MIR

Written for and presented by Itzik Feld and Lucy Levine in the production "Lomir Khasene Hob'n" at the Public Theatre, New York.

I can have most anything in the world that I want; a garden of roses, two suits with four pair of pants. But what I need mostly, is you. I must have, only you.

Lyric by JACOB JACOBS Music by SHOLOM SECUNDA

E Am E
ful mit roy - zn kh'hob tsvey suits mit fir por hoy - zn
itst ge - makht, Der - far shtey ikh itst un ikh trakht, az
Am E7 Am
Nor du, nor du felst mir.
3
3
G7 C G G7
Nu zug ikh bet dikh vos hos - tu oyf mir a zoyns der
Dus vos ikh hob itst ge - makht iz nor a kley - ni -
sf
C
zen? Vos ikh nor fel aykh un ir kent zikh
kayt Az du - vest mir der loy - bn ves - tu

G7
E7
Am
on mir nit ba - geyn.
Ikh hob a hoyz, ikh
zen ikh bin al - right.
Ikh fil ikh darf a
E
Am
E7
hob a pe - tn
Kh'hob a room, ikh
hob tsvey be - tn,
fraynt zeyer ney - tik
Ikh hob tso - ris
ikh hob vey - tik
Am
E7
Am
Nor du,
nor du felst mir
Chorus:
Am
E7
Du felst mir.
Oy oy nor du felst mir.
Oy oy nor

E7
Am
E7
du du du nor du a - leyn.
tr
tr
Am
E7
Du felst mir. Oy oy nor du felst mir. Oy oy nor
Am
du zayt ikh hob dikh der zen Tsvey li - bes
G7
C
Am
to - tshes kley - ne hob ikh ge - hat shoyn fun frier Nor fun zey

G7
Am
E7
nit keyn ey - ne hot nit ge - totsht dos harts bay mir.
Am
E7
Du felst mir. oy oy nor du felst mir. Oy oy nor
1.
Am
du du du nor du a - leyn.
ff
2.
E7 rit.
Am
du nor du a - leyn.
rit.

EYN MOL IN LEB'N

Introduced by Edmund Zayenda in Louis Freiman's musical "Lakh Un Zay Freylakh" which starred Leo Fuchs at the Public Theatre in New York.

How can you describe that special feeling that is so good?
It was ordained that you shall be my mate,
and such good luck comes but once in a lifetime.

Lyrics by JACOB JACOBS/ISADORE LILLIAN Music by SHOLOM SECUNDA

Moderato
Am
G♯dim
Am
G7
Dos glik kumt tsu ye - dn eyn mol,
Am
D♯dim
E
Eyn mol nor klapt es in dayn tir.
Her - tsu dos glik nor kla - pn,
Am
Am6
E
Zay greyt dos bald tsu kha - pn, Az nit flit dos a - vek fun dir.

Am
E7
Am
A7
Dm
A
Der mentsh ken nit vi - sn keyn mol Vos s'meynt dos e - mes glik far
Dm
Bb
Gm6
dir. Zayt ikh hob dikh ba-shtimt veys ikh
Dm6
E
Am
Dm
E7
rit.
a tempo
S'gres - te glik ba-shert is mir.
a tempo
rit.
Moderato
Am6
E7
Am
Dm
Am
Am6
Eyn mol in le - bn treft zikh a - za glik, Ver ken op -

Am
E
Am6
sha - tsn di mi - nut?
Eyn mol in
E7
Am
C6
Dm
Am
E
le - bn treft zikh a - za glik,
Un ven es
Dm6
E7
Am
F6
D
kumt iz a - zoy gut.
In hi - ml on - ge - shri - bn
F6
tr
D
F6
Am
D7
Az du zolst mayn zi - vig zayn,
Ikh hob dikh oys - ge - kli - bn,

Bm7
rit.
E
a tempo
F6
E
ne - sho - me - mayn.
rit.
a tempo
Am6
E7
Am
C6
Eyn mol in le - bn treft zikh a - za
Dm6
Am6
1.
Dm6
E7
glik, Eyn mol, nor eyn mol un nit
Am
E7
2.
Dm6
E7
A6
mer.
eyn mol un nit mer.
3

FARGES MIKH NIT

Introduced by Molly Picon and Yakob Sussanoff in the production, "Malkele Dem Reb'ns," it is one of the most tender songs in the theater repertoire.
My heart pleads: please do not forget me.
Though we are separated,
our love will keep us close, forever.

Lyric by JACOB JACOBS Music by ABRAHAM ELLSTEIN

Andante Romantico
Gm
Cm6
Gdim
D7
f
Gm Cm6 D7
Voice: Gm
Cm6
Gm
Mit dir li - be shpil ikh un ikh bin ful mit freyd, Un
Ikh zol dir far - ge - sn, s'ken keyn-mol nit ge - shen, Vayl
Cm
Dm
G7
Cm
dokh shten - dik fil ikh mir ve - ln zayn tsu - sheyt, Ikh
dayn um - shul - dik po - nem vet in mayn har - tsn zayn, Du

Cm
D
Gm
halt zikh in eyn shre - kn, mayn harts iz ful mit payn, Az
megst mir hey - lik gloy - bn ikh gib mayn e - rn vort Keyn
A7
D
Gm6
D
ikh vel zikh oyf - ve - kn un du vest mer nit zayn, Dan
an - de - re vet keyn - mol far ne - men do dayn ort Vayl
Gm
Cm6
D
D7
Gm
F7
D
zits ikh in a vin - kl un ikh benk un der - far mayn li - ber ge - denk:
dikh nor lib ikh dikh ne-sho-me mayn, un dayn li - be vet to-mid hey-lik zayn.
Chorus:
Gm
ten.
Cm6
Her vi mayn harts bet, far - ges mikh nit
ten.
p-f

D7
Gm
In layd in frey - dn far ges mikh nit.
Cm6
Vayl ikh blayb ey - bik dayngedenk dos "git"
Gdim 7
D7
Gm
Vu du vest zayn far - ges mikh nit
Bb
F
F7
Far - lo - stu mikh nem - stu mayn ne - sho - me mit mit dir

B♭
D7
Dayn no - men blay - bn vet do in har - tsn tif bay - mir
Gm
Cm6
Dray kley - ne ver - ter ge - denk zey "git"
1.
2.
Gdim7
D7
Gm
Cm6
D7
Gm
Cm6
Gm
Ikh bet bay dir, Far - ges Mikh Nit.
Nit.

GALITSYE

The best known Litvak of his day, Aaron Lebedeff was not one to alienate his Galician audiences. He performed this song especially at fund raising benefits in the theater and elsewhere.

Oh what has happened to my poor Galitsye?
Never have I seen so much suffering, so much pain.

Lyrics by MORRIS RUND Music by AARON LEBEDEFF

Andante
Intro:
Am E7 Am
C G7 C
Am Dm Am Dm6
Am
C Am Am6 Am Dm
ten.
Fun Ga - li - tsye, frayn - de, kum ikh itst tsu fo - rn. Un breng aykh fun dor - tn a -
Am Em Am Am6
ten.
tsind a ge - ris. Op - ge - hi - tn zolt ir zayn fun dem tso - rn. Tsu

Dm
B
E7
Am
3
ze - en dort di tso - res, git in harts a ris. Es gey - en dort
3
Dm6
Am
Dm
D7
G7
um le - be - di - ke mey - sim. Groys un shrek-lekh iz dort di
C
Dm
D7
G
G♯dim
noyt. Men far-zetst di tfi - ln un ta - ley - sim.
Am
D7
E
Men-tshn gey - en oys far a shti - kl broyt!

Chorus: a tempo
Am
Dm
Oy, vos es iz ge - vo - rn fun Ga - li - tsye?
Am
A - les iz tse - shtert dort, un far - brent.
Dm
Oy, vos es iz ge - vo - rn fun Ga - li - tsye.
Ir
Am
E7
Am
Dm
D7
G
volt dos, frayn-de, mer shoyn nit der - kent.
Tse - bro-khn ye - des bey-me - le, tse-

C
F
D7
G7
vor - fn ye - des hey - me - le, vu men - tshn fle - gn le - bn zikh ba -
C
Dm
E7
kvem.
Vu ge - ven a shti - be - le,
Am
F
Dm
C7
zet men itst a gri - be - le. A tel ge - vo - rn iz fun der al - ter
1.2.
Am
3.
Am
Dm
A
heym.
heym.
3
3
largo
ff

Glik

"Der Letster Tantz" starring Mikhel Mikhalesko and Bella Meisell at the Prospect Theatre in the Bronx, introduced this great standard.
Good fortune, why did you reach me so late?
You provided but a moment of joy.
But I won't think of what tomorrow may bring,
as long as we have these brief moments together.

Lyric by BELLA MEISELL   Music by ALEXANDER OLSHANETSKY

Moderato
Eb G7 Cm G7
Ikh shtey a-tzind un trakht. Vos far a shtar-ke makht,
Cm Fm6 Bb7 Eb
der shik-zal hot oyf ye-dn men-tchn.
C7 Fm Fm6
Ot makht er zikh a shpas, ot vert er bald in kas,

Cm Fm F♯dim G7 Cm
er ken dikh shtro-fn un oykh ben - tchn. Ven s'iz on mir ge vent,
G7 Cm Fm6 B♭7 E♭
ven ikh volt nor ge-kent, dayn mod-nem shik-zal do far tre - tn.
C7 Fm D7 G7
Volt ikh dikh yetst ba-frayt. Dayn le - bn oykh ba-nayt,
Cm Fm6 D7 G7
un far dayn glik volt ikh ge - be - tn.

Valse lento
Cm
Ab
Cm
Glik, du bist ge - ku - men tsu mir, o - ber a
C7
Fm
bi - sl tsu shpet.
Glik, du host ge -
Db7
Fm
G7
nu - men un far - shaft mayn harts a - zoy fil freyd.
Cm
Ab
Cm
Kh'vil yetst gor - nit kle - rn, vos der mor-gn vet bren-gen far

Ab6
Fm6
G7
Cm6
mir.
A-zoy lang ikh hob khotch eyn mo-ment, dos glik yetst in
Adim
Fm6
D7
1. G7
Cm
C7
Fm
G
may-ne hent, un ikh tants dem lets-tn tants mit dir.
Maestoso
2. G7
Cm
lets-tn tants mit dir.
ff
3
Cm
rit.

GIT MIR OP MAZ'L-TOV

Menachem Rubin, as the father of the bride, introduced this sentimental title song in the Public Theatre production in which he co-starred with Itzik Feld.
Congratulate me, this is my happiest day.
All my dreams have come true,
for I am the father of the bride.

Words by ISADORE LILLIAN   Music by SHOLOM SECUNDA

Andante
G
Fm6
G
Cm
G
Cm
Ven a kind hoybt on tsu ve - rn fer - tsn fif - tsn yor.
G
Fm6
G7
Vet ir ta - te ma - me he - rn un zikh vin - tchn nor.
Cm
G7
Fm6
G7
Got zol mir nor yo - rn ge - bn, dos vintch ikh a - tsind.

Fm G7 Fm G
Kh'zol der - le - bn tsu der khu - pe fi - rn nokh mayn kind. Un
Cm Fm6 Cm Fm6
ven der zi - vig vert in hi - ml dort ba - shtimt, Un men filt az der ba - sher - ter
Cm Fm6 Cm Fm
kumt, Ta - te ma - me's her - tser ve - rn ful mit freyd. Men
Fm6 G7 G
leygt zikh far dem kind a - vek In der leng un in der breyt. Di

Cm G
ma - ma greyt oys-shtey-er, der ta - ta greyt na - dn, Keyn zakh iz nit tsu tay - er dos
Cm G Cm Gm Fm6 Cm
kind zol glik - lekh zayn; Un iz mit ma - zl shoyn ba - shtimt der
Fm D7 G
tog Git der me - khi - tn mit groys shtolts a zog:
Refrain:
G Fm6 G
Git mir op ma - zl tov Shpilt mir a

Fm6
G
Cm
frey - lekhs oyf, Vayl ikh vil frier far a - le
G
Ab
G
Fm6
geyn tan - tsn mit der ka - le. Vayl ikh hob haynt der-lebt
G
Fm6
G
Ab
zen dos vos kh'hob ge-shtrebt un - ter der khu - pe zi tsu
G
Cm
zen. Vi gut s'iz der - le - bn ot di sho, Keyn gre - se - re

Cm
G
Fm
G
Cm
freyd iz gor ni - to, Es iz a ge - di - le az a - fi - le a - le
G
Fm
A♭
G7
Cm
may - ne so - nim bin ikh moy-khl haynt. Zol ye - der haynt mayn na - khes
Fm
D7
Cm
Fm6
A♭6
zen, Un zol di gan - tse velt zikh freyen nu git a tants a ti - pe
G7
Fm
G
1.
2.G
lo - mir tsu der khi - pe geyn ma - zl tov. tov.

A HEYMISHER BULGAR

Actually this song was written for a Seymour Rechzeit recording for RCA-Victor. It immediately attracted many artists to perform it in vaudeville, concert, and club dates.
Let's dance as we used to in the old hometown.
Forget your troubles, as you dance with your friends.

Words and Music by ABRAHAM ELLSTEIN

Dm
Dm
tsar.
Tantst dem tants fun freyd un na - khes,
A - le son - im oyf tsu la - khes, Yi - dn, tantst dem
3
3
Bdim
E
hey - mi - shn bul - gar.
Ge - nug ge - troy - ert,
tr
tan - tsn vi - ln mir.
E
Klez - mer, shvaygt nit,

A7
Dm
git zikh shoyn a rir,
Blozt dos fley - tl,
To Coda
klapt di ta - tsn, rayst di stru - nes biz tsum pla - tsn. A
3
3
Bdim
E
Am
hey - mi - shn bul - gar dos tan - tsn mir,
Shoyn hun - der - ter
tr
E
Bdim
E
Am
mol dikh ge - yogt Yis - rol,
Ge - li - tn fun

E
B7
3
E
Am
so - nim, dos hos - tu shoyn on a - tsol, Nor to - mid iz
3
Dm
un - dzer shtre - bn nor tsu le - bn, Un got zin - gen a shir. To
Dm6
E
shrayt-zhe hoykh mit mut un koykh, Vayl ey - bik le - bn mir.
Interlude:
Am6
Nu tantst un hul - yet, Yi - dn, Der tants vet zayn a gu - ter si - men,
tr
tr

Am6
E7
Tantst dan vi es - fle - gn di o - ves fun a mol. Nu
Am6
tantst un freyt zikh, Yi - dn, Dan vet Mo - shi - akh gi - kher ku - men,
Am
F#7
B
L'sho - no ha - bo ve - ln mir tan - tsn in Erets - Yis - rol.
Coda
Dm
rit.
E
Hey - mi - shn bul - gar dos tan - tsn mir.
rit.

HOPKELE

The finale of the first act of the operetta, "Vus Meydlakh Toen" written for Molly Picon at the Second Avenue Theatre, and performed by Molly Picon, Gertie Bulman, Sam Kasten, and Seymour Rechzeit, who later recorded it and made it a hit.
Let's all join and dance, the "Hopkele."
Forget our worries, and enjoy life.
Girls and boys take partners,
for life itself is just a dance.

Lyric by JACOB JACOBS Music by ALEXANDER OLSHANETSKY

Slow
A7
Dm F6 Bb7 A7 Dm F6 Bb7 A7
Ta - tes, ma - mes shtre - bn zey-ere kin - der oys - tsu - ge - bn,
Dm F6 E7 A7 Dm Bb7 A C7
Vayl dos iz di gres - te freyd bay zey; Un
Fm C7 Fm C7
3
az Got helft zey ze - en un - ter der khu - pe dos kind shtey - en, Git der
3

Dm
Bb7
A7
D
E
A7
ta - te tsu di klez - mer a ge - shrey:
Nu lo - mir
Chorus:
Bright
D
a - le tan - tsn its - ter do a hop - ke - le a shey - ner
A7
D
A7
Bm6
A7
hop - ke - le nu gi - kher: hop, hop, hop, hop! Dos
D
gan - tse le - bn hot der vert a bob - ke - le nu lo - mir

Gm D A7 D D7
geyn a ten - tsl, vi lang es lozt zikh nokh. Oy, oy, oy, gut, ___
___ voyl, ___ lo - mir a - le tan - tsn do in
D G G7
ri - tem, Ot a - zoy gut, ___ voyl, ___
Gm6 A7
3 3
___ mey - dl, nem a bo-kher un tants mit im. Nu lo - mir

D
a - le tan - tsn its - ter do a hop - ke - le, a sheyn - er
A7 D A7 Bm6 A7
hop - ke - le, Nu gi - kher hop, hop, hop, hop! Dos
D Gm
gan - tse le - bn hot der vert a bob - ke - le, Dos gan - tse le - bn iz dokh
D A7 1. D A7 D E A7 2. D
nit mer vi a tants. Nu lo - mir tants.

IKH BIN A MAME

The queen of melodrama, Jennie Goldstein inspired tearful songs such as this one, which she introduced in Louis Freiman's, "Ir Groyser Sod" at the People's Theatre on the Bowery.
I am a mother, but where is my child? Mothers, can you sympathize with me as I feel this humiliation and pain, as I atone for my big sin and live with my big secret?

Lyric by JENNIE GOLDSTEIN/MORRIS RUND Music by J. JAFFE *Arranged by Alexander Olshanetsky*

Andante
Dm
D
Cm6
3
D
Voice:
D
Eb6
D7
Eb
Edim
D
Vos bet a ma - me, ye - dn tog, baym oyf - shteyn un__ baym ley - gn:
D
Eb6
D7
Eb
Cm
D
oy, Got-en-yu, ikh bet__ bay dir, far may - ne kin - ders ve - gn.___ Mayn

Gm
D
tokh - ter, tsu der khu - pe fi - rn, mit ma - zl un ha - tslo - khe. In
Gm
khu - pe - kley - dl zi - ba — tsi - rn, ge - bn ir mayn bro - khe. Ir
Gm
E♭
D
hel - fn on - ton dos khu - pe - kren - tsl oyf ir likh - tik po - nem. Un
Cm
D7
Cm
D
ta - te - ma - me geyn a ten - tsl, zikh frey - en mit ma - khe - to - nim. Kayn

Recit.
Gm
gre-ser glik ken gor nit ge - bn.
Ven ta-te-ma-me dem na-khes der-le - bn.
Vi groys iz di sim-khe, vi groys iz di freyd?
Gm6
Cm
Nor ikh bin far-shol-tn, fun Got un fun
D
Chorus
Gm
layt.— Ikh bin a ma - me, nor vu iz mayn kind?
Ikh bin a
D7
Gm
G7
ma - me, ikh laid far a zind.
Ikh bin a ma - me, muz fun vay-tn

Cm Cm6 Gm A7 E♭7 D7
shteyn; A khu-pe, un di ma-me tor der-bay nit zayn. Ikh bin a
Gm D7
ma - me, s'iz mir nit ba-shert, Vi ye-de ma-me zayn ge-libt un ge-
Gm Bdim Cm
ert. Oy filt ir, ma - mes, mayn vey-tik a - tsind? A shve-re
E♭ E♭7 D7
1. Gm
2. Gm
shtrof tsu zayn a ma-me on a kind. Ikh bin a kind.

IKH HOB DIKH

Aaron Lebedeff was not only a stage star and recording artist, but the highlight attraction of any concert. Consequently he needed songs for all of these activities. His unusual talent for matching lyricists and composers brought him many hits including this one.
Oh how I love to place you on a pedestal!
You are my sun, my moon, my one and only!

Words by KHAYIM TAUBER Music by SHOLOM SECUNDA

E
Am
biz a - tsind?
A - za groy - se mey - dl, du
(groy - ser bo - kher)
E7
Am
D
D7
G
megst zikh — she - men, mir dos khay - es a - roys - tsu - ne - men, un
G#dim
E
G7
mir nit zo - gn az du host mikh: A - za zind. — In
Moderato
C
Dm6
C
Dm6
1. kim - pet iz ge - li - gn mayn tsung un hot ge -
2. ikh hob oys - ge - fi - nen, ikh gey a - rop fun

C
Dm6
shvi - gn. Oy, zo - gn dir az ikh hob dikh. Oy
zi - nen. Ikh hob der - zen az ikh hob dikh. Mayn
1.
G7 C
2.
Dm6 E7 Am
hob ikh nit ge - kent, Biz harts vert azh far - brent:
Moderato
E7 Am E7 Am E7 Am
Zog, zog, zog, di li - be ver - ter, zog mir, mey - de - le, oyf
(bo - khe - rl)
E7 Dm6 E7 Am E7 Am Dm6 E
gikh. Kh'bin zikh moy - de, lyu - be, ikh hob dikh:

Chorus:
E Dm6 E Dm6
Oy, oy, ikh hob dikh, oy, oy, oy, oy, ikh
p-ff
E E Am E Am G♯dim
hob dikh. Zog du host mikh, zog du host mikh oy-khet
E E Dm6 E
lib. Oy, oy, ikh darf dikh,
Dm E E Am E Am
zog zhe lyu-be oykh az du darfst mikh, ikh dikh, du mikh

G♯dim
E
Am
Dm6
zayn ge - tray— biz tsum grib.
Bist mayn zun un mayn le -
Am
Am
Dm6
Am
vo - ne.
Bist fun hi - ml a ma - to - ne.
Bist mayn ne -
Am
cresc.
E
Am
Bdim
E
rall.
D♯dim
sho-me, mayn khay - es, ikh zog es, ikh shray es: Ge - vald! ikh hob dikh a - zoy
cresc.
rall.

E
E
a tempo
F
tr
E
lib.
Oy,
oy
ikh
hob
dikh,
3
a tempo
E
Dm6
tr
E
Am
E
Am
oy, oy, oy ikh hob dikh,
Zog du host mikh,
G♯dim 7
1.
E
2.
E
zog du host mikh oy-khet lib.
lib.

IKH VEL VART'N OYF DIR

A last minute addition to a show starring Menashe Skulnick at the Hopkinson Theatre in Brooklyn, this ballad remains, though the show itself is long forgotten.

I will wait for you, all of my life,
every minute of the day.
For the rest of my life, forever and ever.

Words by ISADORE LILLIAN Music by ABRAHAM ELLSTEIN

Andante
Dm7 E7 Gdim Dm Dm7 A7
f
Dm Gm6 A7
Klin-gen vet mir shten-dik in di oye - rn Az du host mir ge-zogt az du
Dm A7 Dm Am
libst mikh nit, Un dokh hof ikh, ikh hob dikh nit far - loy - rn, Der-mo-nen

E7
A7
3
Gm6
dikh vel ikh a ye-der mi-nut. Ikh veys du host an an-de-re ge-
F
E7
A7
tro - fn, Un du meynst az ye-ner iz dayn glik, Ikh
Dm
Am
B♭
A7
hob dikh e-mes lib un ikh vel ho - fn, As du vest tsu mir ku-men tsu-
Dm
Gm6
Dm
E7
ten.
A7
rik. Her ne-sho-me mayn du zolst vi - sn zayn

Refrain:
Dm
A7
Ikh vel var-tn oyf dir, meg es ne-men vi lang Ikh vel
Dm
Cm6
D7
var-tn oyf dir vayl du bist mayn far-lang Ikh vel var-tn oyf dir
Gm
C7
yedn tog ye-de sho Meg es doy-rn fil yo-rn meg Ikh ve-rn alt un
F
A7
Dm
A7
gro, Oy lu-be nyu. Ikh vel var-tn oyf dir biz di lets-te mi-nut.

B♭m
C7
F
Vayl kayn tsvey - te dayn platz far ne-men vet nit
A7
f
Dm
A7
Dm
D
D7
Host ge - roybt mayn harts mayn glik Un du must es bren-gen tsu -
1.
Gm
B♭
Dm
A7
Dm
A
Dm
rik Vayl Ikh lib nor dikh vel Ikh var - tn oyf dir Ikh vel
2.
Gm
Dm
Bdim7
A7
Dm
D
rik Vayl Ikh lib nor dikh vel Ikh var - tn oyf dir
rit.
ff

IKH VIL ES HER'N NOKHAMOL

Featured in the William Seigel musical comedy "Ikh Bin Farlibt" which starred Menashe Skulnick at the Second Avenue Theatre in New York. This song was introduced by Leon Liebgold and Lilly Lilliana.
I want you to say it over and over again.
I want to hear it loud and clear.
And I will join you in proclaiming,
"I love you, only you."

Lyrics by JACOB JACOBS/ISADORE LILLIAN Music by ABRAHAM ELLSTEIN

Moderato
Fm6
G7
A♭
Fm6
G7
Cm
Fm6
G7
Es ze - nen oyf der velt far - a - nen fil bi - kher ro -
Cm
Fm6
Cm
D7
ma - nen, Fun groy - se lib - es dor - tn ley - nen mir.

G7 Cm Fm6 G7
Lyu-be mayne megst zayn zi - kher az di a - le
A♭ Fm6 D7 G7 Cm
bi - kher ke-nen nit far-shray-bn dos vos ikh fil tsu dir
Dm accel. B♭7 E♭
Meyn-stu vos du zogst tsu reds - tu glat a - zoy.
Ddim rit. G7 Cm
Ikh vil in dem zayn zi-kher vayl Ikh bin a froy

Fm6
Cm
Ge-shvoy - rn dir on tsol un du fregst nokh - a-
ff
D7
rit.
Fm6
Dm7
G7
mol Ikh zol dir zo-gn az ikh hob dikh lib Ikh
Chorus: Slow
Cm
D7♭5
Dm7
G7
vil es he - rn nokh - a - mol fun dir Zog
Fm6
G7
Cm
nokh - a - mol du bist far - libt in mir Es

Fm
Cm
klingt in may - ne oye - rn vi dos shir - ha shir - im lid, tsu
D7
G
Fm6
G7
he - rn dos vel ikh nit ve - rn mid
Es
Cm
D7♭5
Dm7
G7
tantst in mir dos harts fun glik un freyd
C7
Fm
Ven ikh her fun dir di zi - se reyd

Fm6
Cm
Fm6
Ven du zogst di ver - ter fir fil glik far - shaft es mir, yo
1.
G
G7
Cm
G7
Kh'vil es he - rn nokh - a - mol fun dir.
2.
G
G7
C
Kh'vil es he - rn nokh - a - mol fun dir.
ff

IKH ZING

Created for the film "Mamele" which starred Molly Picon. Edmund Zayenda sang the song in the picture.
I sing to you from my heart.
I sing of my love, my dreams.
I sing of my loneliness and of my hope that you will be mine.

Lyric by MOLLY PICON Music by ABRAHAM ELLSTEIN

Andante
G G6 Am D7 G Am7 D7
f
Recit.
G6 Bm C6 G
Shloy-me ha-me-lekh hot-tsu zayn Shu - la - mis ge zin-gen a li - bes shir, Un
C6 G A7 D7
punkt_vi Shloy-me dan,ge lib - te may - ne breng ikh mayn lid_itst tsu dir.

Refrain:
G Em C6 D7 G Em Am
Ikh zing far dir mayn shir ha - shi - rim Mit li - be ikh ba -
Bm E7 Cm6 D7 G Em C6 D7
tsir - im, Far dir nor ne - sho - me mayn Ikh
ff
G Em C6 D7 G Em Am
zing far dir may - ne kha - loy - mes. Mayn li - be vi a
Bm E7 Cm6 D7 G G7
troym iz fun dir nor ne - kho - me mayn

Cm6 G G7
Ven ikh gey oys fun ben-ken nokh dir ge - lib - te mayn. Un
Cm6 G E Cm6 D7
ven ikh halt in eyn den-ken az du vest nokh a - mol may-ne zayn. Ikh
G Em C6 D7 G Em Am Bm ten. E7
zing fun har-tsn may - ne li-der Mayn shir ha - shi - rim vi-der ge -
1. Cm6 D7 G C6 D7 2. Cm6 Bm G Cm6 G
lib-te far dir ikh zing. Ikh lib-te far dir ikh zing.
f
ff

IN A KLEYN SHTIBELE

Introduced by the romantic tenor, William Schwartz, in the musical "Di Goldene Kaleh," which co-starred Lucy Finkel, at the Second Avenue Theatre in New York.
In our tiny cottage, just you and I will live. You were sent to me from heaven to share our love in our tiny home.

Lyric by ISADORE LILLIAN Music by JOSEPH RUMSHINSKY

Moderato
Intro:
C7
F
Ikh denk fun dir tog un nakht, du
Du bist der bal-zam fun mayn harts
mp
rit.
F6
Dm
Dm
C
host mir zu - nen shayn ge-brakht, Di - a - na.
Du far heylst dem gres - tn shmerts mayn Bey-nish.
Ler-nen ken ikh mer nit neyn, zayt
Ley-dn un in frey-dn nor der
F
Dm
G7
C
Gm
dan ven ikh hob dikh der-zen, Di - a - na.
toyt ken undz tsu-shey-dn du mayn Bey - nish.
Zog ge - lib - te hostu ge-benkt oy
Ikh lib dikh mit mayn gan - tsn fay-er

F
Bb
Bbm6
ikh hob fun dir fil ge-denkt, Di - a - na.
du nor du bist bay mir tay - er, Bey-nish.
On dir zayn ken ikh kayn mi - nut, mit
Du bist, du bist, mayn gants le - bn,
G7
C
rit.
dir, mit dir, iz ze - yer gut, Di - a - na: Mir ve - ln
nor far dir vel ikh shtre - bn, Bey - nish: Mir ve - ln
rit.
Moderato
F
C7
voy - nen in a kleyn shti - be - le nor ikh un du mit
F
Bb
F
un-dzer li - be - le Him-lish iz di li - be, du host mir der - kvikt.

C7
F
Got hot dir fun hi-ml mir a-rop ge - shikt. Mir ve-ln voy - nen
C7
in a kleyn shti - be - le nor ikh un du mit un-dzer li - be-
Slower
F
rall.
B♭m
F
le. Ven ikh vel ve-rn alt un gro, un ku-men vet mayn lets-te sho, vet mayn lets-
rall.
C7
G
C7
1.
F
2.
F
te vort zayn ikh hob dikh lib. Mir ve-ln lib.

KH'BET DIKH HOB MIKH LIB

Introduced by Leon Gold and Anna Toback in the operetta "Dos Freylikhe Shtetele" which starred Menashe Skulnick at the Second Avenue Theatre in New York.
I beg you, please love me.
I cannot live without your love.
And if you love me, I'll return your love ten-fold.

Lyric by ISADORE LILLIAN Music by JOSEPH RUMSHINSKY

E7
Am
E
hemd
Du meyn nit az ikh freg vos tut men mit di teg, Ikh
E7
Am
A7
freg dikh nor vos tut men mit di nekht? A klog is mir a brokh
Dm
E7
dayn man bin ikh dokh. Far - vos ba - han-dlst du mikh a - zoy shlekht?
Am
Dm6
rit.
Am6
E7
Oy vos bis - tu kalt tsu mir? Oy, ge - vald ikh bet bay dir.
rit.

Refrain:
Am
Kh'bet dikh hob mikh lib kh'bet dikh hob mikh lib
F6
E
On dayn li - be zols - tu vi - sn trayb - stu mikh in grib.
E
Kh'bet dikh hob mikh lib az nit ver ikh dil
Am
Am6
Lib mikh un ikh vel dikh li - bn tsen mol a - zoy fil

Am
Kh'bet dikh hob mikh lib
bet ikh zikh bay dir
Nem mikh nit a-
Dm
roys dos harts der - ba - rem zikh oyf mir
Zog mir az du host mikh ge - rn
Am
E7
az nit vel ikh me - shu - ge ve - rn Tznu - e ey - ne, ma - me shey - ne
1. Am
Kh'bet dikh hob mikh lib.
2. Am rit.
Kh'bet dikh hob mikh lib.
8
rit.

LIBE

Although this was originally written for a show, it did not become well-known until Seymour Rechzeit started to perform it on the radio and later recorded it for RCA-Victor.
Love, what are you really like?
What are you really made of?
You enter the heart, spin the head,
and life without you becomes impossible.

Words by MOLLY PICON   Music by ABRAHAM ELLSTEIN

Andante
Fm
Gdim
D♭6
C7
Fm
p recit.
C7
Fm
B♭m
S'iz mir oy - fn har - tsn shver, Oys - hal - tn ken ikh nit mer,
Fm
C7
D♭7
C7
Khotsh es mu - tchet un es tsit dokh iz es a - zoy gut.
rit.

Fm
Eb7
Ab6
Ye - der gart un hoft un vart oyf dir
Ab
Gb6
F7
Men veyst nit ven du kumst tsu - geyn, Du
Em6
Bbm
gan - vest zikh a - rayn. Shpe-ter heybt men on tsu
Eb7
rit.
Ab
C7
zen Az siz shver on dir tsu zayn.
rit.
3

Chorus:
Fm
C7
Li - be, ver hot dikh oys-ge-trakht, Li - be,
Fm
B♭m
fun vos bis-tu ge-makht, Ye-des glid es tsit un brit far
C
C7
Fm
dir
Li - be,
C7
du krikhst in harts a-rayn Li - be, far-dreyst dem kop vi vayn

Fm
Li - be, bist vi a kin - der troym,
C7
Fm
rit.
Li - be, Bist vi a laykh-ter shoym a ga-ney - dn
rit.
Bbm
1. C7 rit.
Fm
C7
far a ye - dn iz di Li - be nor
rit.
3
2. C7 rit.
Fm
iz di Li - be nor
rit.
3

MAYN MAZ'LDIKER TOG

The title song from the musical which starred Irving Jacobson, Miriam Kressyn, Edmund Zayenda, Lucy Gehrman, and Selma Kaye.
I'll never forget when I met you.
You are the sunshine of my life.
My lucky day was when you returned my love.

Lyrics by JACOB JACOBS   Music by JOSEPH RUMSHINSKY

Am Am6 Em Am6 Em6 B7
ven, Oy, ye - nem tog far - ge - sn ken ikh nit
Em B7 Em Am6 Em E7
neyn. A shey - ne tsu - kunft hot zikh in mayn
Am D D7
fan - ta - zi tse - shpilt, A zi - se li - be in mayn har - tsn
Em B Em
hob ikh bald der - filt. My Luck - y Day dem sod ikh

B7
trog, My Luck - y Day, der ma - zl - di - ker
Em
1.
2.
Em
Fine
tog. My Luck - y
Mayn ma - zl - di - ker
Verse:
Em6
Gdim
Em
Ven ikh bin a - leyn mit zikh - nor fun dir ikh trakht,
Em6
B7
Em
Un ikh dank dem shik - zal vos hot dikh tzu mir ge - brakht.

B7
Glik - lekh hos - tu mikh ge - makht___ zayt du bist mayn fraynd, Du
B7
bist dos likht, der shtral vos hot_ mayn_ le - bn mir ba - shaynt. Mayn
Am6 B7 Am6 B7
tay - re, mayn li - ber, Ikh gib zikh dir i - ber.
Am6 B7 Em D. S. al Fine
Ah,
My Luck - y
Mayn ma - zl - di - ker

MAYN YIDISHE MEYDELE

The title song of Anshel Schorr's production at the Liberty Theatre in Brownsville, which starred Dora Weissman, Menashe Skulnick, William Schwartz, and Anna Toback.
My Jewish girl, how lovely she is! Search the world over and you'll never discover another like her and with her charm.

Lyrics by ANSHEL SCHORR   Music by SHOLOM SECUNDA

Am 6 C♯dim B G C♯dim D7 G
vi di froy bay dem Yi - dn. A Yi - dish mey - dl mit ir blik, far -
Am A7 D7 G C♯dim
ki - shift bald in gan - tsen dikh. Un gis - tu nor oyf
D7 G Em Am F7 B
rit.
ir a kuk, fil - stu a Yi - di - shn tam in zikh. Mayn Yi - di - she
rit.
Moderato
Chorus:
Em B B7
mey - de - le, zi iz a - zoy sheyn. Mayn Yi - di - she

Em
E7
meydele, mit ir Yidishn kheyn. Fun gold ire
Am
Em
herelekh, di tseyn ner vi perelekh, nor a Yidishe
Am6
B7
Em
E
Am
meydl ken zayn azoy sheyn. Ir vet far milyonen,

Am6
Em
bay an - dre nats - yo - nen, nit ge - fin - en a
Am6
1.
B7
Em
Am F♯
mey - dl, mit a Yi - di - shn kheyn.
B7
2.
B7
Em
Mayn Yi - di - she mit a Yi - di - shn kheyn.
a tempo

MAZ'L

A great standard, this song made its initial appearance in the film "Mamele," which starred Molly Picon. Since then it has been widely recorded by many artists, among them: The Barry Sisters, Jan Peerce, Seymour Rechzeit, as well as the lyricist and the composer themselves.

Good fortune has come along for others, why does it avoid me?
Will it ever come and will it as it has for others bring a little happiness to me.

Lyric by MOLLY PICON   Music by ABRAHAM ELLSTEIN

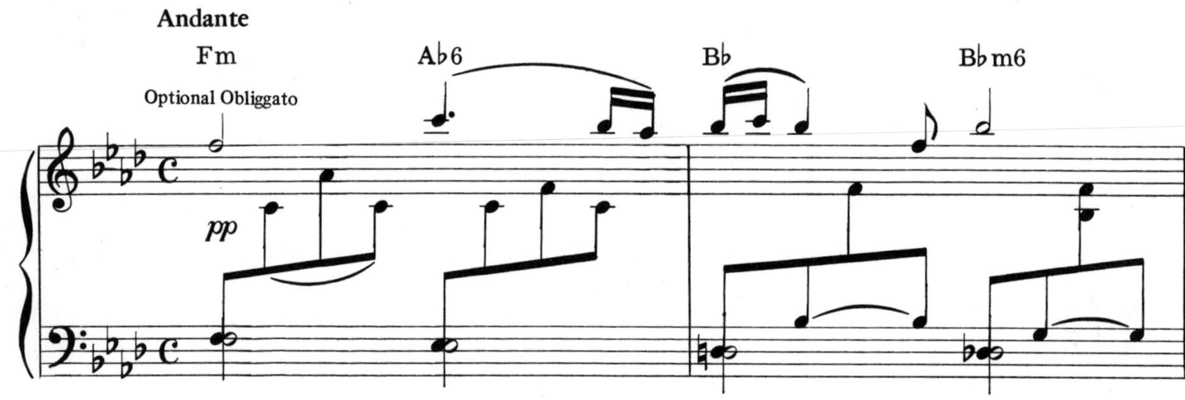

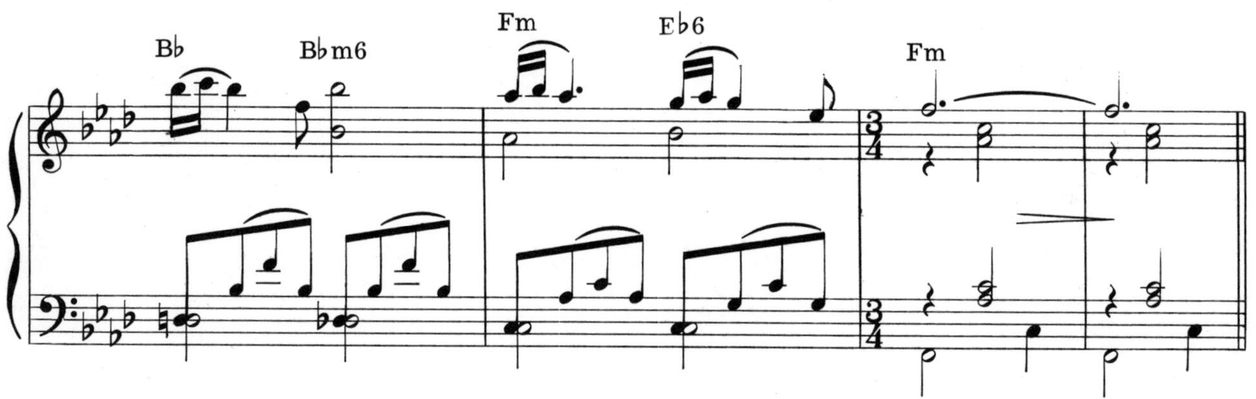

Refrain:
Fm
C7
Ma - zl, es shaynt a mol far ye - dn
Fm
Far ye - dn nor nit far mir
C7
Ma - zl, du brengst a - ye - dn frey - dn
Fm
Far - vos far - zoym - stu mayn tir ?

F7
Bbm
Oy vi es tut bank a ye - de sho
Dos
Eb7
Ab
C7
le - bn far - geyt, un kayn hof - e - nung iz alts ni - to, oy,
Fm
C7
Ma - zl, es shaynt a mol far ye - dn
Fm
Fine
Far ye - dn nor nit far mir.
8va

Verse:
Fm
C7
Fm
Ven es kumt on di nakht Blayb ikh zi - tsn un
C7
Fm
B♭m6
Fm
trakht, Nokh a tog iz shoyn vi - der far - bay,
F7
B♭m
F7
B♭m
Un der kho - lem vos ikh hob ge - kho - lemt far
F7
B♭m
Bdim
C
C7
D. S. al Fine
zikh Iz a - vek mi - tn vint oyf dos nay.
rit.

MEYDELE

Written for Seymour Rechzeit to sing in vaudeville and concert and on the air. After he recorded it for RCA-Victor, the song was widely featured by other artists.
My lovely girl, you illuminate my life.
Your magic takes away all my sorrow.
I love you, my lovely girl.

Lyric by JACOB JACOBS   Music by ABRAHAM ELLSTEIN

Bb6
Am
Am6
Gm6
Adim
D7
ven iz mayn le-bn fil yo-rn ge-kveylt, Vayl do in mayn har-tsn hot e-pes ge-felt. Zayt
Bbm6
F
G7
F6
G7
C7
du bist ge-ku-men, mayn lib mey-de-le, Ho - stu ye-de vund oys-ge-heylt.
rit.
Chorus: Con sentimento
F
F♯dim
Mey - de-le
(Yin - ge-le)
Zayt du bist do tsu mir in
sf
C7
Gm6
harts a-rayn
Mey - de-le
(Yin - ge-le)

Gm
Am
F
accel.
Du host ge - brakht mir glik un - zu - nen - shayn
Vayl ikh vel
accel.
Bb
Bbaug
ke - nen shten - dik zikh der - kvi - kn
Mit day - ne zi - se
Gm
Bbm
G7
C
li - bes - bli - kn
Vos ve - ln mikh ba - gli - kn nor a - leyn.
C7
Caug
F
F#dim
Mey - de - le,
(Yin - ge - le)
far vos hobn mir zikh nit ba -
rit.
a tempo

C7
Gm
Cm6
ge - gnt frier
Mey - de - le
(Yin - ge - le)
dayn bild iz oys - ge-kritst in
D7
Gm
Gm6
A
harts bay mir
Du host mir ayn - ge - ge - bn
a nay le - bn, Mayn
Dm
G7–9
F
1.
C7
velt ge - makht mir klor,
Mayn mey - de - le,
(yin - ge - le)
zol zayn oyf lan - ge
ff
F
C7
2.
C7
F
yor.
zol zayn oyf lan - ge yor.

A MEYDELE VI DU

Introduced by Leon Liebgold in William Seigel's musical comedy "Ikh Bin Farlibt" which starred Menashe Skulnick and was presented at the Second Avenue Theatre in New York.

I am unworthy of this angel which heaven has sent me.

Who can compare with her? And soon she will be mine forever.

Lyrics by ISADORE LILLIAN/JACOB JACOBS Music by ABRAHAM ELLSTEIN

G Cm G G7 Cm G7
Ikh gib tsum him-l a blik, Got hot ge-shikt mir a glik Der
Cm G7 rit. Cm G Cm Dm7♭5
ta-yer-er oy-tser fun him-l iz mir nor ba - shert
rit.
Chorus: Slow
G Fm7 G Fm7 G
Mayn mey-de-le iz a mey-de-le ful mit kheyn
yin-ge-le
Fm6 G7 A♭7 G7 A♭7
Fun mayn mey-de-le iz nokh she-ners nokh

G G7 Cm A♭7
nit ge - veyn Kuk ikh in i - re
G7 Cm A♭7 G7
oy - gn tzvey, Punkt vi tzvey shte - rn fin - klen zey. Es
Fm6
brengt mir freyd ir ye - de mi - ne, Oyf ir po - nem rit de shkhi - ne
G Fm6 G Cm
nor Oy

Cm6 G7 Cm Cm6 G7
ver ken zikh tsu mir glay-khn, Az ikh hob ge-kent der-grey-khn
Cm D7
a - za glik Me - ka - ne iz mir ye - der ey - ner
3
G Fm6
do Mit ma - zl vil ikh
G7 rit.
di a - ksu - be un - ter shray - b'n, Un der nokh vet

Fm6
G7
Fm7
zi oyf a - le mol far - blay - b'n Mayn mey - de - le,
G7
Fm7
Dm7♭5
ta - yer mey - de - le, vet zayn may - ne in a gu - te
1.G
2.G
Cm
A♭7
sho.
sho. Mayn mey - de -
G
Fm
G
Fm
G
le.

MIT DIR IZ MIR GUT

H. Kalmanovich's musical comedy "Maz'l-Tov, Molly" which starred Molly Picon, and in which Leon Liebgold and Anne Winters had featured roles, provided Liebgold with this song.
When you're with me I have everything I need.
You make my life worthwhile,
you're the highlight of my life.

Lyric by MOLLY PICON   Music by JOSEPH RUMSHINSKY

Fm
Fm6
Fm
Mit dir bin ikh shtolts,
Mit dir hob ikh
Mit dir ken ikh zayn,
Er - lekh, gut un
Dbm7
C7
tr
Fm
C7
alts,
Ma - me - le,
kh'o dikh,
kh'o dikh
fayn,
Ma - me - le,
kh'o dikh,
kh'o dikh
3
Fm
Eb7
Ab6
lib.
Ikh ken punkt vi
lib.
Far eyn blik fun
Bbdim
Ab
Moi - she Ra - bey - nu
Shpal - tn ya - men oykh,
day - ne eyg - lekh
Ken ikh a - les ton,

A♭6
B♭m6
E♭7
Bay mir iz ni - to keyn da - yey - nu, Punkt vi Shim - shon
Vi di zin - gen - di - ke feyg - lekh Glaykh in hi - ml
C
C7
Fm
Fm6
hob ikh koykh. Ven ikh bin mit dir ye - de sho
ken ikh flien. Ven ikh bin mit dir ye - des yor
8va
Fm
D♭m7
C7
tr
Fm
C7
Iz gan - ey - dn do,
Iz a re - ge gor.
8va
3
Ma - me-le, kh'o dikh, kh'o dikh
Ma - me-le, kh'o dikh, kh'o dikh
8
1.
Fm
C7
lib.
2.
Fm
rit. B♭
B♭m
Fm
lib, ikh hob dikh lib.
rit.

NARISHE TATES

The title song of a musical drama which starred Ludwig Satz at the newly built Yiddish Folk Theatre on Second Avenue in New York.

Foolish fathers how long will you sacrifice yourselves?
Work and struggle for your families, but for what?
To remain forever, the fool!

Words by ISADORE LILLIAN Music by ABRAHAM ELLSTEIN

E Dm6 E Dm6 E
Her, li - ber bru - der, vos ikh zog dir Vos toyg de -
Dm6 E Dm6
ba - tes, Men plogt zikh far kin - der der - nokh blay - bn mir
E7 Am
na - ri - she ta - tes. Vos du host far deyń zun ge - trayt alts un ge - tin Ge -

G♯dim
Am
E7
volt zikh ma - krev zayn - far kin - der, In ka-ledzh im ge-shikt, Du
host a - roys ge-kukt oyf na - khes, Un vos hos - tu, zog, a - tsin - der? Vu
G♯dim
E7
Am
ken men tre - fn, vu, A - za ta - tn vi du. Du bist dokh a - me - shu - ge - ner, ikh
Dm
Am
Dm
D7
veys es, Es loynt zikh nit, ikh shray, Tsu zayn a - zoy ge - tray, Vos
G
C
E7
Am

E7
Am
E
D♯dim
hot men fun di kin-der, Got - veyst es. Ge - zorgt zikh un far-borgt zikh un
E
D♯dim
Am
rit.
E7
nit ge-hat kayn ru, Ge- yogt zikh un ge-plogt zikh, Un ge - bli- bn yetst bis-tu A
rit.
Refrain:
Am
B
E
E7
na - ri-sher ta-te Vi vild du bist Na-ri-sher
Am
Dm
Dm6
ta - te, Veyst vos du tust, Host ge - op-fert zikh far

E7 Am Dm Am
kin - der Un vos hos - tu a - tsin - der Ayn - zen muz - stu
Am6 Dm E7 Am
its - ter az du bist A na - ri - sher
B E E7
ta - te, Kuk zikh nor tsu Na - ri - sher

Am
Dm
ta - te, um - zist dayn mi
Ven dayn zin - dl vet a
G♯dim
C
F6
Dm6
ta - te ve - rn, Di zel - be ver - ter vet er he - rn: A na - ri - sher
E7
1.
Am
2.
Am
Dm6
Am
ta - te bist - tu.
tu.

OY MAME, BIN IKH FARLIBT

Written for a record session with Molly Picon, the Barry Sisters recorded this song twice: once for RCA-Victor as the Bagelman Sisters and later for Cadence as the Barry Sisters.
Oh, Mama am I in love! It's the boy who plays the fiddle who's always on my mind. I'm so excited, I'm in seventh heaven. I want to embrace the whole world.

Words and Music by ABRAHAM ELLSTEIN

Em
zay - ne shey - ne shvar - tse oy - gn Hot er dan mir tsu - ge - tsoy - gn,
Em6 B7 Em B7
Oy, ma - me, voyl un gut iz mir.
Em
Un ven er zogt "hey du mey - dl" Bist dokh a - zoy lib un ey - dl,
Em
Un zayn shpil - in krikht in har - tsn a - rayn,

Em
tr
Vilt zikh tan - tsn, vilt zikh zin - gen, Oy, ge - vald, ikh ver tze-shprin - gen,
Em6
B7
Em
B7
On im, oy, ken ikh mer nit zayn:
(Not too fast)
Chorus:
Em
Oy, ma - me, bin ikh far - libt,
p-ff
Em
E7
Am
Oy, ma - me, bin ikh far - libt, A

C6 Cm D7 G Cm G
klez - mer - yin - gl, ma - me ge-tray - e, ligt mir nor in zin, Ikh
Am6 B7 Edim B B7
veyn un lakh un veys nit, ma - me, Oyf vel - kher velt ikh bin.
Em
Oy, ma - me, bin ikh far - libt,

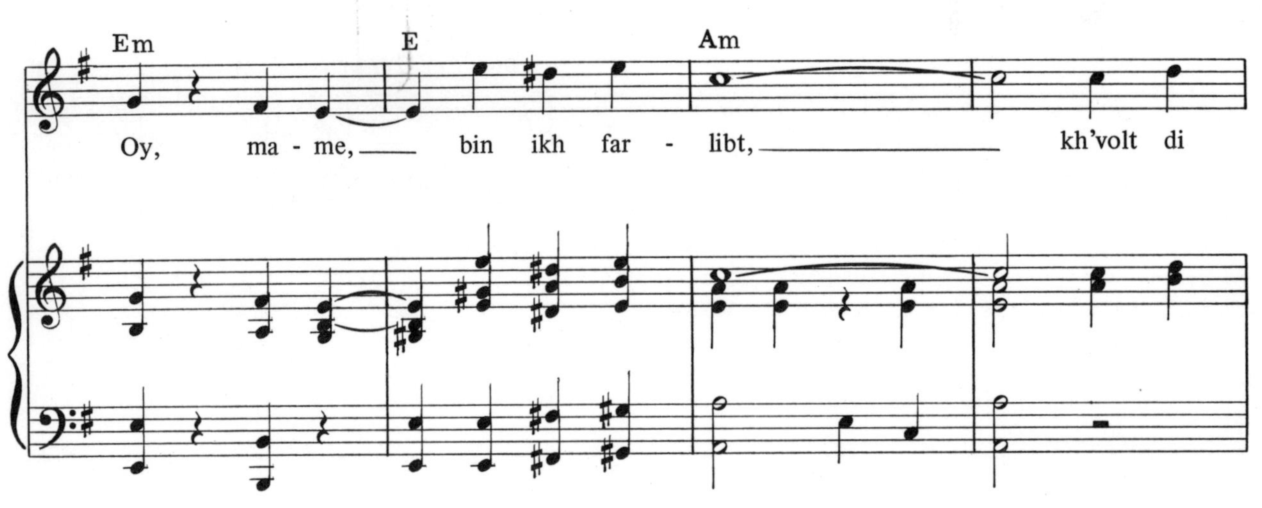

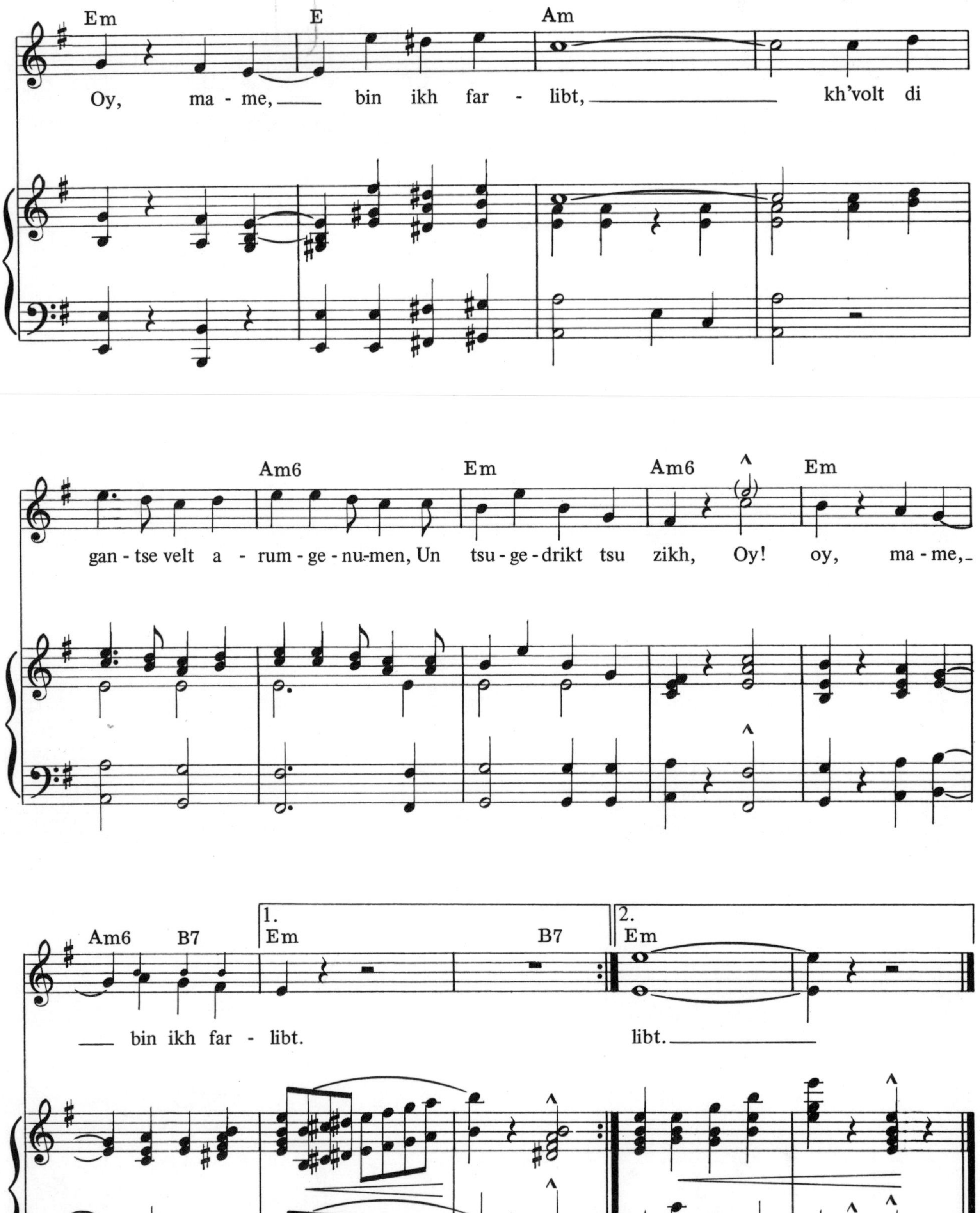

Em E Am
Oy, ma - me, bin ikh far - libt, kh'volt di
Am6 Em Am6 Em
gan - tse velt a - rum - ge - nu-men, Un tsu - ge - drikt tsu zikh, Oy! oy, ma - me,
Am6 B7
1. Em B7
2. Em
bin ikh far - libt.
libt.

Oy S'iz Gut

An impressive team brought "Mayn Malkele" to the stage of Public Theatre in New York. The stars, Molly Picon and Aaron Lebedeff; the librettist, William Seigel; the director, Jacob Kalich.
How good it is to be with your loved one!
How marvelous, when your head starts to spin!
How good it is to say, "I love you."

Lyric by JACOB JACOBS Music by ABRAHAM ELLSTEIN

Fm6
Fm
E♭6
Ven zi flegt on hey - bn re - dn fun ye - ne tsayt vos s'iz ge - ven mit
Fun ir likh - tik zi - sn po - nem vos iz fil mit yi - d' - shn
Fm
Fm6
G7
Cm
rit.
dir In i - re oy - gn hot men bald der - kent Dem
kheyn Ye - des mol vos kh'gib oyf dir a kuk Der -
rit.
Fm6
G7
Cm
C7
Fm
fink vos hot bay ir in harts ge - brent. Oy Zi flegt mak - hn a - za mi - ne vi
mont dos mir in mayn far - loy - rn glik, Vayl du host dayn ma - mes oy - gn vos
Fm6
Fm
E♭6
Fm
s'volt oyf ir ge - rut di shkhi - ne G'ven iz zi dan glik - lekh on a shir.
shay - nen vi a - re - gn boy - gn She - ne - re hob ikh keyn mol ge - zen

Bb
Eb7
Ab
Bb
C7
Day-ne ver-ter klin-gen gut on shir
kh'bet dir zog zi nokh a-mol tsu mir
Chorus:
Fm
Fm6
Fm
Oy s'iz gut!
Aleyn tsu zi-tsn mit a mey-dl, yin-gl,
Oy s'iz gut!
Fm6
C7
Der kop far-dreyt zikh vi a re-dl
Kri-gn a ke-di-shn rin-gl
Oy s'iz gut!
Ven me ken a mey-dl yin-gl zo-gn
Fm
C7
Fm
kh'hob dikh lib
Oy s'iz gut!

Fm6
Fm
Fm6
tr
flegt mayn ma-me shten-dik zo-gn
Oy s'iz gut!
A sod in har-tsn um-tsu-tro-gn
tr
C7
Fm
Oy s'iz gut!
Tsu zayn a bal-e-bos bay zikh a-leyn in shtub
Ab
Eb7
Ab
Dbm
Oy
kh'hob shoyn dem be-stn si-men as du bist er-lekh
Ab
Fm
fayn
Oy
zayt du bist on-ge-ku-men

Fm6
C7
Fm
bis - tu mir glaykh a - rayn in di bey - ner. Oy s'iz gut!
tr
ven men ken di ver- ter he - rn Oy s'iz gut! ven s'iz nish - to ver zol shte - rn
C7
di mi - nut Tyokh - ket do bay mir in har - tsn
1. Fm
C7
2. Fm
C7
Fm
Oy s'iz gut! Oy s'iz gut! Oy s'iz gut!
ff

OYG'N

Molly Picon composed this song for herself to present in Jacob Kalich's production, "Eyn Mol In Leb'n" at the Public Theatre in New York.

Your dazzling, compelling eyes have attracted my heart.
No longer am I depressed, as I respond to the allure of your ecstatic, dark eyes.

Lyric by MOLLY PICON Music by ABRAHAM ELLSTEIN

F Bb m6 F Bb m6 F
S'iz a fin - ste-re nakht un ikh zits mir un trakht mayn_ le - bn hot
Bb6 F Eb dim Gm Cm6 Gm
gor - nit kayn vert. S'iz ley - dik un pust mayn shtre - bn um-
Cm6 Gm G7 C7 Fm
sist kayn_ ma - zl iz mir nit ba - shert. Nor plits - im a
accel.

C7 Fm C7 F Bb♭m6 F7 Bb♭m F Gb♭7
shtral, a likh - ti - ker kval, tsvey oy - gn hob ikh der - zen.
Gb♭ Fm6
Ikh hob bald der filt, mayn
sf
Bb♭ Ab♭ Bb♭m6 Fm Eb♭ Db♭ C7
harts iz far shpilt, nor ikh bin tsu - fri - dn ge - ven.
Fm C7
Oy - gn far day-ne, shvar - tse, oy-gn far zey shteyt

Bbm6
C7
3
Fm
ayn - ge - boy - gn di likh - ti - ke zun.
F7
Bbm
Eb
Oy-gn far day-ne, shvar - tse, oy - gn zay ho - bn
Eb7
Ab
Ebm6
tsu - ge - stoy - gn mayn harts un ikh bin far shklaft ge-
F
F7
Bbm
Bbdim
vo - rn. Oyf mayn gants le - bn far - gaft ge -

Eb
Eb7
Ab
Fm
G7
Edim
vo - rn un ikh vel shtrebn a - les zey tsu ge - bn.
rit.
Fm
C7
Oy - gn far day - ne, shvar - tse, oy - gn
Bbm6
C7
di velt vet mer nit toy - gn on day - ne shvar - tse
1.
Fm
C7
2.
Fm
C7
Fm
oy - gn.
oy - gn.

ROZHINKES MIT MANDL'N

A poignant lullaby from the first Yiddish musical production, "Shulamith."
Beneath Yidele's cradle is a young, white goat. When it goes to market so will you, to deal with your raisins and almonds. But for now, hushabye, my son.

Words and Music by ABRAHAM GOLDFADEN *Arranged by Henry Lefkowitch*

Moderato
Dm Am Dm A7 Dm
f
Dm Am Dm Am
In dem beys ha - mik - dosh, in a vin - kl khey - der zitst di al -
E7 A C7
mo - ne, Bas Tzi - on a - leyn. Ir ben yo - khi - dl,

F Gdim F Dm6
Yi - de - len, vigt zi ki - sey - der, un zingt im tzum shlo - fn a
A7 Dm Gm6 Dm
li - de - le sheyn. Ah! Un - ter
Chorus:
Dm F Dm6 Dm
Yi - de - les vi - ge - le. Shteyt a klor va - ys
A F A7
tsi - ge - le. Dos tsi - ge - le iz ge - fo - rn

Dm
Gm
Dm
hand - len.
Dos vet zayn dayn ba - ruf
A7
Dm
A7
ro - zhin - kes mit mand - len.
Shlof - zhe,
1.
2.
Dm
Ddim
B♭
Yi - de - le, Shlof.
Shlof.
A7
Optional ending
Dm
Gm6
Dm
Shlof.

RUMANIA, RUMANIA

One of the great standards of the stage, Lebedeff wrote this song over a period of years, adding and deleting material in response to the audiences. Finally set by Sholom Secunda, it was recorded by Lebedeff and many other stars.

Oh, Rumania, you were once a wonderful land, where it was a pleasure to live, and to delight in the joys of wine, women, and comradery.

Words and Music by AARON LEBEDEFF *Arranged by Sholom Secunda*

C6 D7 G 3
G6 Cm6 D7 G
mol a land a zi-se, a shey-ne.
Ekh, Ru-
tr
me-nye,Ru-me-nye,Ru-me-nye,Ru-me-nye,Ru-me - nye,Ru-me-nye, Ru - me - nye.
Ge-ven a
pp
C6 D7 G 3
C6 D7 G
mol a land a zi-se, a fay-ne.
Dort tsu
tr
G
G 3
voy-nen iz a far-ge-ni-gn.
Vos dos harts glust dir, dos kens-tu kri-gn.
A ma-me-
sf
sf

D7 G C rit. D7 G
li - ge - le, a pas-tra - me - le, a kar - na - tse - le, un a gle - ze - le vayn, a - ha!
pp
Allegro moderato
Gm
In Ru - me - nye iz dokh gut, fun keyn day - ges
zor - gn
ff
tr
D7 Gm
veyst_ men nit; Vayn_ trinkt men i - be - ral,_ me_ far - bayst_ mit
a
D7 Gm Cm6 D
kash - ta - val. Hay di - gi di - gi dam, di - gi di - gi di - gi dam;
kas - tra - vet.

Gm
D7
Gm
Hay di - gi di - gi di - gi di - gi - di - gi dam; Hay di - gi di - gi dam
Cm6
D
Gm
D7
Gm
di - gi di - gi di - gi dam; Hay di - gi di - gi di - gi di - gi di - gi dam.
G
Oy vey g'vald, ikh ver me - shi - ge,
Di Ru - me - ner trin - ken vayn un
kh'lib nor brin - ze, ma - me - li - ge, kh'tants un frey zikh biz der stel - ye,
e - sn ma - me - li - ge Ver es kusht zayn ey - gn vayb, o

D7
G
ven ikh es a pat - lo - zhe - le.
ye - ner iz me - shi - ge.
Dzing - ma, tay ti - dl di dam;
ff
pp
Dzing - ma, tay ti - dl di dam; Dzing - ma, tay ti - dl di dam;
D7 G D7 G D7
Dzing-ma, tay ti - dl di dam. Ay, s'iz a me - kha - ye, be - ser
G D7 G D7 G D7 G D7 G
ken nit zayn, ay, a far - ge - ni - gn iz nor Ru - me - nish vayn.

Allegro Vivo
G
A
Yo - kum pur - kon
D
G
min she - may - e, shteyt un kusht di kekh - ne, Kha - ye, on - ge - ton in
D7
G
al - te shkra - bes, makht a ku - gl l'ko - ved Sha - bes. Zets! tay
D7
G
ti - dl di dam; Zets! tay ti - dl di dam; Zets! tay

D7
G
D
ti - dl di dam; Zets! tay ti - dl di dam! Ay, s'iz
G
D7
G D7 G D7
a me - khay - e be - ser ken nit zayn, ay, a
G
D7
G D7 G
far - ge - ni - gn iz nor Ru - me - nish vayn. Ay
G
ay ay.
ff
sf

SHEYN VI DI L'VONE

Menashe Skulnick used to say that this song was written for him to sing, but now that it is a big hit and everyone sings it, he has stopped.

Like the moon above you, the stars remind me of you
The angels knew I love you, so heaven sent you to me.

Lyric by KHAYIM TAUBER Music by JOSEPH RUMSHINSKY

Moderato
Fm
Bbm6 Fm
Der moych iz mir tsu misht. Ikh
gey a-rum tse-khisht. Kh'veys a-lein nit vos ikh vil.
Bbm6
Gm6
C6
mf
Bbm
Ebm6 Bbm
Ebm6
Eb7
Ab
C7
Kh'shem zikh, ikh bin royt. Di tsung iz bay mir toyt. Kh'ken nisht zu-gn, vos ikh fil. Du

Fm Bbm6 Fm Bbm6 Bbm6 Fm C
bist a-rayn tsu mir, in har-tsen oyf kvar-tir kh'trakht vi tsu zo - gn dir, az du bist. . .
Chorus:
Fm Fm
Sheyn vi di le - vo - ne, likh - tik vi di
Bbm
shte - rn. Fun hi - ml a ma to - ne,
Fm Bbm Fm C7 Fm
bis - tu mir tsu - ge - shikt. Mayn glik hob ikh ge -

Fm
vi - nen, ven ikh hob dikh ge - fi - nen.
B♭m
Fm
B♭m C7
Shaynst vi toy - znt zi - nen, host mayn harts ba -
Fm
B♭m B♭m6
B♭m B♭m6
glikt. Day - ne tseyn - de - lekh, vay - se pe - re - lekh,
B♭m
E♭7
A♭
mit day - ne shey - ne oy - gn, day - ne kley - de - lekh

Ab Db Eb6 C7
day - ne he - re - lekh, host - mikh tsu - ge - tsoy - gn.
Fm
Sheyn vi di le - vo - ne, likh - tik vi di
Bbm
shte - rn. Fun hi - ml a - ma - to - ne,
Fm Bbm C7 1. Fm C7 2. Fm Bbm Fm
bist - tu mir tsu - ge - shikt. shikt.

A SHEYNER KHOLEM

New York's Public Theater had a large marquee, but hardly enough room to list the stars from this show: Aaron Lebedeff, Itzik Feld, Lucy Levine, Yetta Zwerling, Leon Gold, David Medoff, and many more.

It was all a beautiful dream,
How rude was the awakening?
Yet I hope that my sweet, romantic dream may someday come true.

Words by ISADORE LILLIAN Music by SHOLOM SECUNDA

Gm A7 D7 Gm
Akh vi du vest fe - ln mir
Moderato
Bb F7 Bb G G7
Tsu a - le tso - res vet ku - men a sof Biz dan mayn li - be
Cm F
vart un hof In mayn harts ve - stu nor zayn a - leyn.
Bb Bb7
Kh'vel ben - ken shtark nokh dir mayn glik Un

Very slow
portamento
G
G7
Cm
Cm6
F7
ef - sher ves - tu gor - nit ku - men tsu - rik Kh'vel vey - nen kh'vel
B♭
Gm
Cm
D7
Gm
mey - nen Az es iz a kho-lem nor ge ven A shey-ner
Gm
D7
kho - lem iz dus ge - ven A zi - ser
D7
Gm
kho - lem vi vun - der sheyn Ikh hob ge -

Gm
Cm
kho - lemt ikh hob ge - klert Zol nor der
Gm
E♭
D7
Gm
kho - lem nit ve - rn tsu - shtert Kh'ze un - dzer
Cm
F
B♭
G7
glik in kho - lem Ikh hof az Got vet ba - she - rn Az un - dzer
Cm
D
shey - ner kho - lem Vet nokh a virk - lekh - kayt ve - rn A shey - ner

Gm
D7
kho - lem gelibte mayn Ze az der
ge - lib - ter
1.
Gm
kho - lem zol e - mes zayn.
Gm
2.
D7
Gm
D7
Gm
A shey - ner zol e - mes zayn.

SHTARKER FUN LIBE

The romantic leitmotif of the Menashe Skulnick hit "Punkt Mayn Maz'l" at the Second Avenue Theatre in New York. It was sung in the show by Leon Liebgold and Lilly Lilliana.
The bond between lovers,
the heat of passion, the ardor and ecstasy,
forever prove that nothing is stronger than love.

Lyrics by JACOB JACOBS/ISADORE LILLIAN   Music by ABRAHAM ELLSTEIN

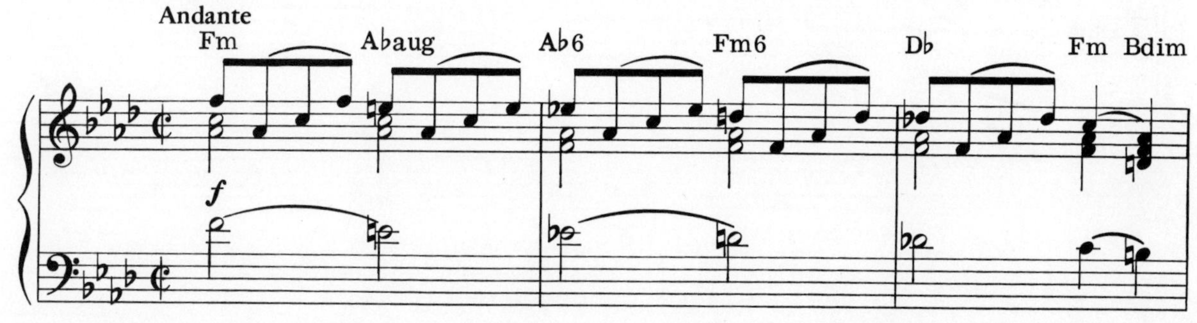

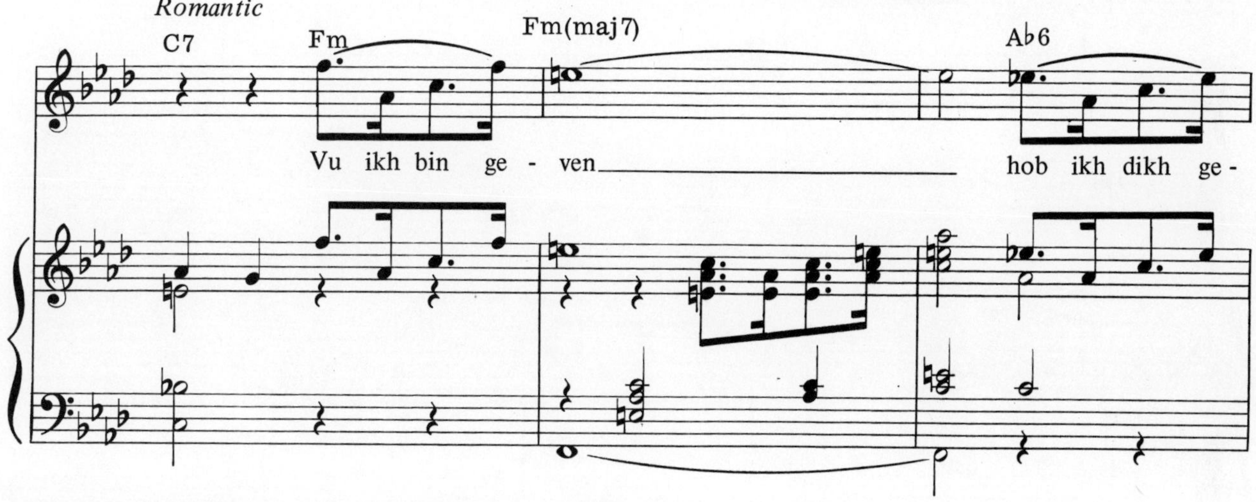

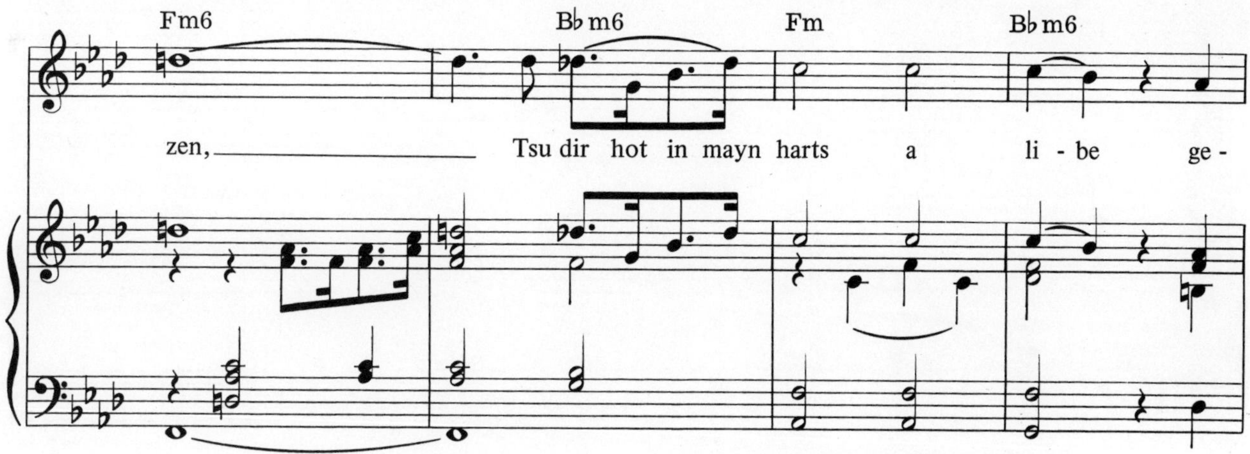

C7 C Edim7
brent. Zog mir, lib - ster mayn, zog vi ken dos
Ab6 Fm6 Bbm Gbm C7
zayn, Host dokh mikh a - fi - le nit ge -
Fm Fm(maj7) Ab6
kent, In mayn fan - ta - zi G'kho-lemt i-mer
Fm6 Bbm6 Ebm6
tsu Hob Ikh fun a mey - de - le punkt a - zoy vi
3
3

E♭m6
B♭m
Edim
du. Bare - khn un ba - trakht vi shtark iz li - bes
Fm6
B♭m6
G
makht, Frem - de her - tser tsvey tsu - noyf - ge -
Fm6
Gdim
Fdim
C
brakht.
Chorus:
D♭
Fm
Vos ken zayn shtar - ker fun li - be? ? Dos fregt men shoyn toy - zn - ter

C7
Edim
C7
yor,
Vos ken zayn shtar - ker fun li - be?
Ven
Fm
D♭
Fm
s've - rn far - ey - nikt a por.
Far ir iz keyn kor - bn tsu
F7
B♭m
vey - nik,
Far li - be vert ey - ner oys ke - nig.
Kha -
B♭m6
Fm
B♭m6
loy - mes zikh ve - bn, es makht zis dos le - bn Ven s'kumt on di

C7 Fm Ab
glik - le - khe sho. Mayn li - be iz hey - lik un
Bbm6 Bb6 Eb7 Ab6
ta - yer Zi fla - kert un glit um - ge - hay - er.
Db Fm Bbm6
Der flam iz an ey - bi - ker fa - yer, Vayl keyn
G7 C7 1. Fm G7 C7 2. Fm
shtar - ker fun li - be z'nish - to. to.

SHVER TZU ZAYN A YID

The title song of Harry Rothpearl's production of Sholom Aleykhem's story. Joseph Buloff and Miriam Kressyn starred and marked Sholom Secunda's final contribution to the Yiddish theater.
It's hard to be a Jew and be persecuted at every turn. Life is sometimes bitter and hopeless, but you, God remain our shield and our protector.

Lyric by ITZKHOK PERLOV Music by SHOLOM SECUNDA

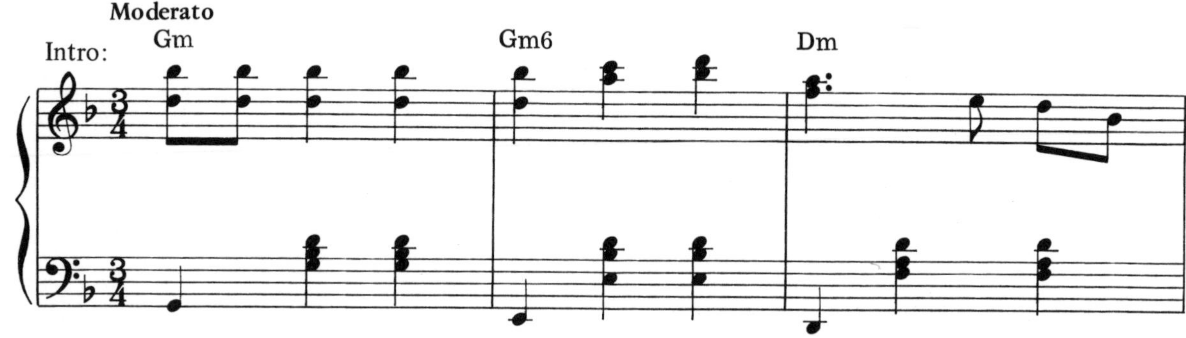

Gm
Gm6
Dm
D7
Gm
Kuk a - rop fun hi - ml un ze.
Me yogt day - ne
Gm6
Dm
F
B♭7
kin - der, me plogt day - ne kin - der. Oy her un - dzer bi - ter ge -
A7
Gm
Gm6
A7
shray.
Ha - bet mi - sho - ma - yim u - rey.

Chorus:
Dm
F♯dim
Gm
S'iz shver tsu zayn a Yid. Me
Gm6
A7
Dm
Dm
D7
brent undz do di trit. Mir klo-gn un mir lyar-men, ven
Gm
Gm6
A
ves-tu zikh der-bar-men, oy Ta-te, oy Fo-ter ge-tray-er? Du

Cm6 D Gm C7
varfst fun va - ser undz in fay - er. S'iz undz bi - ter, s'iz nisht
F A7 D E♭dim Gm B♭
gut. Du bist dokh un - dzer got un be - fray - er, Oy S'iz
1. Dm A Dm
shver tsu zayn a Yid.
2. Dm6 A7 Dm
S'iz shver tus zayn a Yid.

SLUTZK

The show palace of Second Avenue New York was the new Public Theater where the best companies played one operetta after another. Mischa and Celia Boodkin introduced this song and later took it with them all over the world.

Slutsk my hometown, you lie deep in my heart.
How I miss you and my many childhood experiences.

Words by AARON LEBEDEFF   Music by HERMAN WOHL *Arranged by Sholom Secunda*

Andantino
Gm Cm Gm Eb6 Gm
Recit.
Gm C Cm6
Ikh der - mon zikh its - ter in mayn shte - te - le dem kley - nem,
Fray - tik nakht di ma - me flegt di likht zikh ben - tshn, der
Cm F F7 Bb7
vi ikh hob di shayn tsu ersht der - zen.
ta - te in beys - ha - med - resh flegt zikh geyn.

Eb
Bb
Cm
C7
F7
Vi ikh bin ge - boy - rn dor - tn, vi ikh bin der - tsoy - gn,
Un fun shul oyf sha - bes flegt er bren - gen frem - de men - tshn,
Bb
Eb6
D7
G
Bdim
vi ikh fleg als kind in khey - der geyn;
zmi - res zin - gen, flegt men zey - er sheyn.
Cm
Bb
Cm
C7
F
F7
Vi ikh bin ge - boy - rn dor - tn, vi ikh bin der - tsoy - gn,
Un fun shul oyf sha - bes flegt er bren - gen frem - de men - tshn,
Bb
Eb6
Cm6
D7
G
Gm
vi ikh fleg als kind in khey - der geyn.
zmi - res zin - gen, flegt men zey - er sheyn.

Chorus:
Moderato
Gm Cm Gm Bb Eb
Slutsk, oy Slutsk, mayn shte - te - le, vi ikh benk nokh-dir!
Gm Cm Gm Ab
Tif in har - tsn, heym du mayn, lig - stu do bay mir. A
Cm F7 Bb
vi - gl oyf a shtri - ke - le, un a tse - bro - khn be - te - le;
Bb6 Cm 1. Gm Cm6 Gm Cm 2. Gm rit. Cm6 Gm
Un dokh tay-er bis-tu mir, Slutsk, oy Slutsk, mayn shte-te-le. Slutsk, oy Slutsk, mayn shte-te-le.
rit.

Tif vi di Nakht

Written for the film, "A Brivele Der Mam'n" which starred Mischa and Lucy Gehrman, the popularity of this song can be attributed to the many artists who recorded and presented it all over the world.
Deep as the night was the enchantment that we knew.
The world, that night was a paradise for two.

Words and Music by ABRAHAM ELLSTEIN

Andante Romantico
Em
Gm6
Gaug
L. H.
p
sff
ffz
B7
p
Em
A6
B7
Em
Ven di nakht
kumt tsu geyn
Un ikh blayb
dan a -
p
F♯7
B7
Em
C
leyn
Alts
iz shtil
nor mayn harts
vos benkt on a
3

Em
E7
f
Am7
B7
shir
Dan tsit mikh tsu dir Ge -
3
6
Am7
B7
E7
Am
lib - te kum tsu mir Vi di nakht in ir prakht vos der -
6
rit.
F♯7
3
B7
Em
mont mikh ey - bik fun dir. Tif vi di
rit.
Chorus:
Em6
Am6
3
nakht Iz mayn li - be tsu dir ge - lib - te mayn
3
3
3

B
B7
Tsu zayn mit dir dos iz alts vos ikh ba-
Em
Em6
ger Ikh zits un trakht
Am6
B
tsu dos glik vet mit undz oyf ey - bik zayn Far - lir ikh

B7
Em
Am6
dikh
hot dos le - bn gor kayn vert
Em
E
Dm6
E7
Vi di zun un di le - vo - ne
Vi di shte - rn vos ba -
G#dim
Am6
D7
Cm6
laykht di nakht
A - zoy sheyn iz mayn ma - to - ne

D7
G
Am6
B7
Em
rit.
a tempo
nor fun hi-ml hot dos Got tsu mir geb-rakht. Meg alts ge-shen
rit.
a tempo
Am6
B
B7
p
meg a-fi-le yetst di velt un-ter geyn Mayn li-be vet
rit. ten.
1.
Em
B
Em
2.
Em6
ey-bik zayn, tif vi di nakht.
Tif vi di nakht.
rit.

UNDZER YIDISH FOLK

Introduced by Miriam Kressyn who co-starred with Menashe Skulnick. The timeliness of this song resulted in many recordings by such artists as Seymour Rechzeit, Cantor Liebele Waldman, Cantor Maurice Gantchoff, and others.

The Jewish people will live forever and endure every hardship.

The Jew survives because of his strong faith and devotion.

Lyric by JACOB JACOBS Music by ABRAHAM ELLSTEIN

Gdim Dm E7 Am
li - tn a shrek, Um-tsu - bren-gen hot men im pru - birt. Fun
f C G7 C G7
ye - dn vin - ke - le hert zikh a - tsin - der der vey fun dem Yi - dns gesh -
C E7 Am C#m7♭5 Dm
rey: Go - te - nyu, helf day - ne Yi - di - she kin - der Un
E7 Am f B7
shik a ye - shu - e far zey. She - ma - Yis - ro - el shray - en
f

E
Am
Dm6
E
mir ___ A-doy - shem e - khod, Got, tsu dir.
Refrain: Am
E7
Am
E7
Un-dzer Yi - dish folk vet ey - bik le - bn Un oys - hal - tn ye - dn ge -
p
Am
E7
far, Un - dzer Yi - dish folk hot got ge - ge - bn
Am
Dm
Dm
koy - ech un mut der - far. Men hot undz ge - pruvt mit
3
3

G7
ten.
C
rit.
va - ser un fay - er O - ber tif in har - tsn
rit.
E7
Am
blaybt undz tay - er, Oy, Un - dzer Yi - dish folk vet
Dm6
Dm6
Am
E7
ey - bik le - bn un oys - hal - tn ye - dn ge -
1. Am
E7
2. Am
Dm6
A
far.
far. Un - dzer Yi - dish folk.
ff

VEN IKH KUK OYF DIR

The theme song of the production, "Sadie Was a Lady" which starred Molly Picon with Muni Sereboff at the Second Avenue Theatre in New York.

When I look at you it seems that the sun has just begun to shine.

The whole world is in my grasp, I feel wonderful when I look at you.

Lyric by MOLLY PICON Music by JOSEPH RUMSHINSKY

Andantino
Dm
p
Gm
Gm6
Meyd - lekh kho - le-men kha - loy - mes
ku - men vet a
A
Gm6
man tsu geyn,
Un der man vi in troym iz
C7
F
F♯dim
Gm
to - mid yung un hoykh un sheyn,
Un baym ersh - tn blik zey

D
Adim
Gm
Adim
ve - ln vi - sn shpe - ter o - der frier,
Gm6
E7
A7
Ve - ln zey a khu - pe shte - ln, zo - gn vet er tsu ir:
Moderato
Refrain:
Dm
A7
Dm
Dm6
B♭
A7
Ven ikh kuk oyf dir, gib a blik oyf dir, Ver ikh der - frisht.
Dm
Gm6
Dm
Ven ikh ze dikh geyn, Blaybt dos harts mir shteyn, ikh ver tse - misht.

A7
Dm
E - fn - stu di groy - se, shvar - tse oy - gn day - ne,
Gm
A7
Dm
Dakht zikh mir di zun heybt plu - tsem on tsu shay - nen. Ven ikh kuk oyf dir,
A7
Dm
A7
Gib a blik oyf dir, Ver ikh tse - khisht.
B♭dim
A7
Trakht ikh zikh vi mayn ma - zl - hot mikh ba - glikt,

Bbdim
A
A7
Volt ikh di gan - tse velt Tsum har - tsn
Dm
A7
tsu - ge - drikt, Ver iz glaykh tsu mir? Ikh bin raykh on shir
1.
2.
Dm
A7
Dm
Dm
A
Dm
Ven ikh kuk oyf dir.
Ven ikh kuk oyf dir.

VI AHIN ZOL IKH GEYN?

Born in the cafés of Europe, where it found a place with touring theatrical companies, this song was brought to America by Menashe Oppenheim. It is a world favorite.

Tell me, where can I go?
Seems every door is closed for me.
The Jew is persecuted at every turn,
there is no room for him.

Lyric by O. STROCK Music by S. KORN-TUER

Moderato
Em B7 Em
mf
Der Yid vert ge-yogt un ge-
Am D7
plogt Nisht zi - kher
B7 Em
iz far im ye-der tog
f
Zayn

E7
Am
le - bn iz a fin - ste - re nakht. Zayn
B7
Em
shtre - bn alts far im iz far - makht Far-
E7
Am
lo - zn bloyz mit so - nim, kayn fraynt
B7
Em
Kayn hof - nung on a zi - khe - rn haynt

Refrain:
Em
Vi a - hin zol ikh geyn? Ver kon ent - fe - rn
B7
mir? Vi a - hin zol ikh geyn?
Am
B7
Em
Az far-shlo - sn z'ye - de - tir S'iz di velt groys ge -

E7
Am
nug
Nor far mir iz eng un kleyn
Em6
1.
D♯dim
Vi a blik kh'muz tsu - rik S'iz tzu-shtert ye-de brik Vi a-hin zol ikh
B7
2.
D♯dim
rit.
B7
Em
geyn?
brik Vi a-hin zol ikh geyn?
3
rit.
3

VOS DU VILST, DOS VIL IKH OYKH

Originally presented in the musical comedy "Pinye Fun Pinshev" which starred Itzik Feld at the Public Theater in New York.
Whatever you want, I want too.
I want to fulfill your every desire.
No mate has ever had your charm.
You are my heart and soul.

Lyric by JACOB JACOBS Music by SHOLOM SECUNDA

Verse:
E
Am
Kh'vel dir zo - g'n shoyn, az
Dm6
E
Am
Dm6
du vest zayn mayn kroin. Ikh_ vel dikh tay - e - re tro - g'n oyf mayn
E
Am
Dm6
E
kop. Vest hey lig zayn bay mir, kh'vel shpig l'n zikh in dir. Du

Dm
Dm6
E
Am
bist bay mir fun Got der shens ter gob.
Ikh vel far dir
Am
al - les ge - r'n tohn,
a - bi du zolst mit mir tsu - fri - d'n
E7
Am
Dm
zayn.
Ikh vel mit dir in di him - l'n flien,
Dm6
G♯dim
E
dir bren - g'n dem gan eyd'n - in shtub a - rayn

Chorus:
E Dm D♯dim E
Vos du vilst dos vil ikh oykh, du bist_ mayn harts, mayn moykh. Du
Am E Dm E
bist dos vay - zil fun dem oyg_ bay mir.
E Dm D♯dim E Dm
Kh'hob nor shten-dik eyn ge - dank, ikh hob_ nor eyn far - lang, dos te - le - rl fun
E Dm6 E Am
hi - ml gib_ ikh dir._ Es iz ni - to keyn mey - dl

E7 Am
vos zol ho-bn dayn kheln. Kh'vel zayn a ko - sher vay - bl vi mayn ma-me iz ge -
Vest
E E7 E
ven, oy. Vos du vilst dos vil ikh oykh,
Dm Am E Dm E Dm
tr tr tr
ikh brekh_ zikh itst mayn moykh, az - vos ikh vil dos zol - stu ve - ln
1. 2.
E Dm6 E
oykh. oykh. oykh.

Vos Geven Iz Geven Un Nito

Composed originally for vaudeville star, Sam Klinetsky, who rejected it as being too sentimental, Nellie Casman introduced it as a change of pace for her and it became the sensation of the day.
What used to be, used to be, is no more. How fast our youth passes us by, never to be relived again.

Words and Music by DAVID MEYEROWITZ

Moderato
Am6
E7
Am
ff

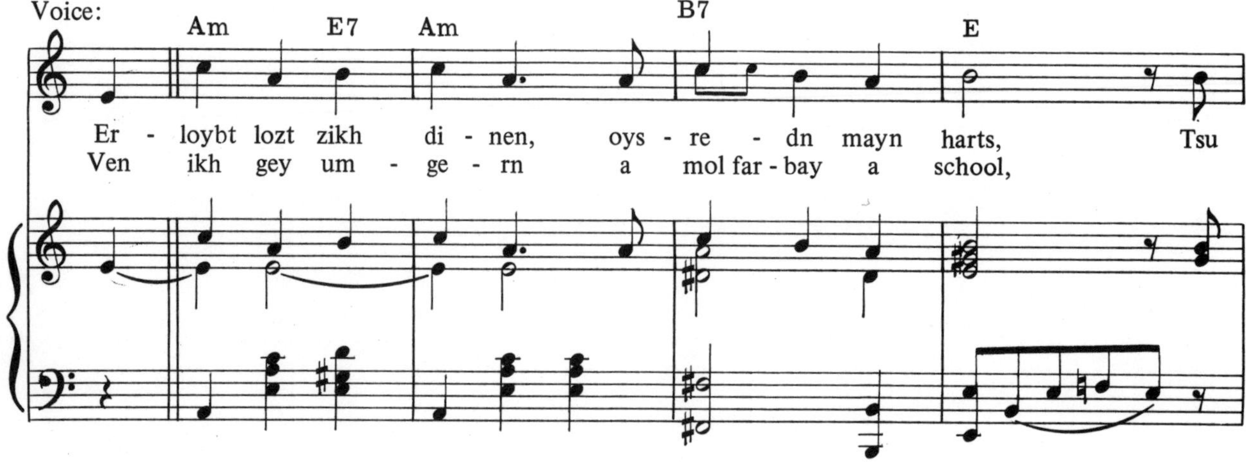

Voice:
Am
E7
Am
B7
E
Er - loybt lozt zikh di - nen, oys - re - dn mayn harts, Tsu
Ven ikh gey um - ge - rn a mol far - bay a school,

E7
Am
E7
E7
Am
red ikh fun zi - nen, Tsu red ikh fun shmertz, Ikh
Gis ikh mit tre - rn, Un trakht fun a - mol, Vi der

C G7 C Am F♯dim E
layd fun a kran - kayt, Vots heyst nit kayn krenk, Men
yung - itch - ker moyekh' l, Zayn glik nit far - shteyt Un
Am Dm7 Am B7 E
ruft es on el - ter, es nogt un es benkt:
kumt men tzum sey - khl, iz dan shoyn tsu shpet: Vos Ge -
Refrain: Am B7 E7 Am
ven Iz Ge - ven Un Ni - to Shoyn a -
Dm G7 C
vek ye - ne yor, ye - ne sho Vi

Am
B7
E7
shnel far flit der yun - ger glik
Un men
Am
B7
E7
ken es nit kha - pn mer tsu - rik
Vayl Vos Ge -
Am
E7
Am
A7
ven Iz Ge - ven Un Ni - to
Di
Dm
A7
Dm
kref - tn ve - rn shvakh, di hor vert gro
Men

G7 C G7 C
neyt zikh, men kleyt zikh, men makht zikh sheyn, Men
3
F Am6 Bdim E7 rall.
nart o - ber key - nem nor zikh a - leyn, Vayl Vos Ge -
rall.
Am Dm6 E7 Am
ven, Iz Ge - ven, Un Ni - to.

VOS IZ GEVOR'N FUN MAYN SHTETELE?

Featured in an operetta, starring Menashe Skulnick at the Hopkinson Theater in Brooklyn and sung by Leon Liebgold and Lilly Lilliana.
What has become of my home-town?
I recall the quaint village streets,
the lush trees of the countryside.
Never more will I see them again.

Lyric by ISADORE LILLIAN Music by ABRAHAM ELLSTEIN

Em Am Em Am B7 Em
Fle-gn mir shpa - tsi - rn geyn Un kho - le - men kha - loy - mes on a tsol.
Bm G B7 Em
Oy, vi de - molt iz ge - ven A - zoy har - tsik a - zoy sheyn
Am6 Em B7 Em E7
Ven mir fle - gn geyn far - bay di shul Un dem kha - zns
Am Cm6 D7 G Em Am
shey - ne shtim Hot ge - klin - gen a - zoy frim Bay dem o - mid mit groys ge -

B7
Recit. Em
fil.
Ke-va
ko-ras ro-ey ed - ro
Em
Ma-vir tso-no ta-khas shiv-to Ma-vir tso-no ta-khas shiv-to ta khas shiv -
toy
Em
Ke - va - ko - ras ro - ey ed - ro Ma - vir tso - no
Bm
F#7♭5
Bm
Em
t a khas shiv to Ma-vir tso-no ta-khas shiv-to Ma-vir tso-no ta-khas shiv-to

B7
Em
a tempo
ta khas ta - khas shiv - to A - za ben - ke - nish fun
a tempo
B7
Em rit.
Am6
B
frier Ge - bli - bn iz in harts bay mir.
rit.
Slow
Refrain:
Em
Am
B7
Vos iz ge - vo - rn fun mayn shte - te - le? Vos iz ge - vo - rn fun mayn al - te
Em
C
B
Em
heym? Oy, vi es benkt zikh nokh mayn shte - te - le, Mayn

Am D7 G
yu-gnt hob ikh dokh far-brakht in dem. Dos ge-se-le dos shu-le-khl, Vi
D7 G Em Em6 B7
har-tsik un vi sheyn, Dos boy-me-le, dos mi-le-khl, Vel ikh es ven nokh zen, Oy?
Em Am Am6 1. Em C C♯dim B
Vos iz ge-vo-rn fun mayn shte-te-le, oy, Vos iz ge-vo-rn fun der al-ter
Em Am C♯dim B 2. Em B B7 Em Am6 Em
heym. iz ge-vo-rn fun der al-ter heym.

VU ZAYNEN MAYNE ZIB'N GUTE YOR?

David Meyerowitz provided many special songs for the vaudevillians of the day. Such artists at Nellie Casman, Rubin Doctor, Louis Kramer and others performed these songs although many of them composed their own.

Where are my seven fruitful years?
If not seven, how about a few?
Will I live long enough to ever attain,
those seven good years?

Words and Music by DAVID MEYEROWITZ

Moderato
Introduction
Eb
Bb
D7
Gm
Cm
D7
Gm
ff
Gm
Cm6
Gm
Cm6
Far aykh, men-tshn muz ikh mikh ba - klo - gn
Fun day - gn vert mir azh groy di
Dem tam fun kap - tsn zol key - ner far - zu - khn,
Es tri - knt di ge - hi - rn oys fun
Gm
Cm
hor,
Ge - hert hob ikh fun fil - e men-tshn zo - gn
Az
moykh,
A kap - tsn tsu a toy - tn iz ge - gli - khn,
Dos

Gm F7 B♭ Cm6 D7
Got git ye - dn zi - bn gu - te yor. A - zoy
zogt di toy - re un ikh zog dos oykh. A
Gm Cm Gm
halt ikh in eyn var - tn un eyn ho - fn, Ikh
mol flegt men di tso - res khotsh far - gi - sn, M'hot zikh
Gm Cm C7
vart ikh ver tse - pi - ket, ikh kra - pir, Un der gut - er yor hot mir nokh nit ge -
on - ge - shi - kert un ge-meynt s'iz gut, bir, shnaps, vayn fun zoy - er un fun
F7 Gm Cm Cm6 D
tro - fn, Iz es meg-lekh az mayn Got zol blo - fn mir?
zi - sn, Un a - fi - le dos er lobt mayn pok - et nit:
Vu

Refrain:
Gm
D7
Gm
zay - nen may - ne zi - bn gu - te yor?
G7
Cm
Oyb nit zi - bn, zol khotsh zayn a por,
E♭6
B♭
D7
Gm
E - pes fun dem le - bn kho - tshe, Iz mayn ne - sho - meden fun a klo - tshe,
Cm
D7
1.
Gm
D7
2.
Gm
Vu zay-nen may-ne zi - bn gu - te yor?
Vu yor?

YUK'L!

Yetta Zwerling introduced this song in a production at the Arch Street Theater in Philadelphia. The song was such a big hit that it firmly established Anshel Schorr as a producer and gave Sholom Secunda his first trip to Europe.

Wherever I go, they tell me my Yuk'l is a fool.
However, fool or not, I need, I want, I must have, my Yuk'l.

Words by ANSHEL SCHORR   Music by SHOLOM SECUNDA

Andantino
G
B
Vamp
Em
B
Voice:
Em
B7
Em
E
Kh'gey a - rum un hob fil tsar, un veys nit vos tsu ton der - far,
S'iz ad - ver - tised a bar - gain day, me - ner hoy - zn a - ler - ley,
Am
Am6
B
Em
Vi ikh gey, un vi ikh shtey, a - rum un a - rum, un u - me - tum,
a sher, a me - ser, un a dre - ser, tsu ker, zalts, un gen - zn shmaltz, keyn

Am6
B
G
B7
veyst men Yu - kl iz a nar.
Un dav ke vayl er iz a
yu - kl krigt men nit oy vey.
Ikh volt-ges pent dem lets - tn
Em
C
F♯7
B
yu - kl,
im a - ye - der li - bn muz.
Ir
cent,
fun mayn poc - ket nor da - fir
ven
G
B7
Em
Am6 G rit. Am6
B
megt aykh vin - tshn a - za yu - kl,
vi mayn Yu - kl iz.
ikh volt kri - gn nor ge - kent,
a yu - ke - le far mir.
rit.
Andantino
Chorus:
Em
tr
Vi bis - tu Yu - kl ey - ner? Vi bis - tu Yu - kl shey - ner?

C♯dim
Edim
B7
Ikh benk a - zoy nokh dir.
Em
Yu - kl, Yu - kl may - ner, Yu - kl, Yu - kl fay - ner,
Edim
Am6
Em
kum shoyn tsu - rik tsu mir.
Am
Ikh ken on dir nit le - bn, ikh vel dir a - les ge - bn,

Am6
Am
Am6
a - bi kum shoyn tsu - rik tsu mir, in a gu - ter sho, oy.
Em
G6
Ikh vel zikh nor ba - gro - bn, ven ikh vel dikh nor ho - bn,
C6
D7
G
B7
1.
Em
2.
Em
vayl nokh a - za min yu - kl, iz oyf der gan - tser velt ni - to. to.

YID'L MIT'N FID'L

The great folk-poet Itzik Manger made one of his rare musical contributions for Abraham Ellstein's film score of the same name

Who knows the two musicians in the haywagon?
Yid'l with his fiddle, Arye and his bass.
All of life is a song, all of life is a game.

Words by ITZIK MANGER Music by ABRAHAM ELLSTEIN

Allegro
Em
Bb
Em Bb
E
B7 Em Bm
ff (Sehr lebedig)
sf
sf
Em Bm Em Em7 Am6 Em Em7
1. I - ber fel - der, ve - gn, oyf a vo - gn
2. A tsig shteyt oyf der lon - ke un me - ket troy - rik:
3. A foy - gl flit: gut - mor - gn, Gut - mor - gn, a gut -
Am6 D7 G6 C
hey. Mit zun un vint un re - gn,
me! Hey, du tsig, du shoy - te,
yor! Di troy - er un di zor - gn tsu

Am6
B7
Em
(Sehr breit)
Em7
fo - rn klez - mer tsvey. A khi - dish, oy, a
troy - rik zayn iz fe! Sho - klt er dos
al - de shvar - tse yor! Dem vint a lakh in
Em6
rit.
C
B7
khi - dish, Zog, ver zey - nen zey?
ber - dl: Ta - ke, ta - ke, fe!
po - nem Un yi - dl, yi - dl, for!
rit.
rit.
a tempo
Refrain:
E
G6
Em6
F#7
Bm
Em6
Yi - dl mi - tn fi - dl, Ar - ye mi - tn

Bm
Em
C
G6
bas, Dos le - bn iz a li - dl, To
Am
C
B
CM7
vo - zhe zayn in kas, hey! Yi - dl, fi - dl,
(Geshrei)
C#7
B7
1.
Em
B7
2.
Em
shmi - dl, hey, Dus le - bn iz a shpas! shpas! Hey!
ffz

ZISE KINDER YOR'N

A not-to-be-forgotten reminiscence of childhood which Meyerowitz fashioned for his huge vaudeville audiences and which was featured by every leading star of the day.

Sweet childhood years will forever remain in my memory.
Too quickly do the years of our youth pass us by.

Adapted from M. Gebirtig by DAVID MEYEROWITZ

B♭
C7
F
Ven ikh trakht fun ay - er tsayt tut mir dan bang un layd,
Ye - der blik fun yen - er tsayt blabt bay mir an ey - bi - keyt,
Dm
Gm
A7
Dm
3
oy, vi shnel ikh hob aykh on - ge - vo - rn.
tif in har - tsn blaybt es ayn - ge - shlo - sn.
3
Interlude: (a little faster)
Dm
Gm
Dm
A7
Dm
Voice:
Gm
Dm
2. Kin - der yo - rn, zi - se blu - men tsu -
4. Ot ze ikh di shub far mayne oy - gn

A7
Dm
rik tsu mir vet ir shoyn mer nit ku - men.
vu ikh bin ge - boy - rn un er - tsoy - gn.
Mir
Bb
C7
F
yo - rn kal - te troy - ri - ke,
al - te mo - re sh'koy - ri - ke
dukht ikh ze mayn vi - gl dort,
shteyt nokh oyf dem zel - bn ort,
Dm
Gm
A7
Dm
D. S. ad lib
ho - bn ay - er shey - nem plats far - nu - men.
wi a kho - lem iz a - les far - floy - gn.

ZUG ES MIR NUKHAMOL

Ludwig Satz and Zina Goldstein introduced this song in the production "Der Berditshiver Khusin" at the Public Theatre in New York.

Tell it to me once again, your words bring happiness to my soul.
Ask me. I'll do anything for you.
I'd become your slave—anything.

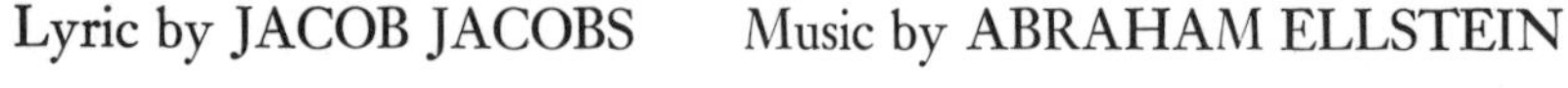

Lyric by JACOB JACOBS Music by ABRAHAM ELLSTEIN

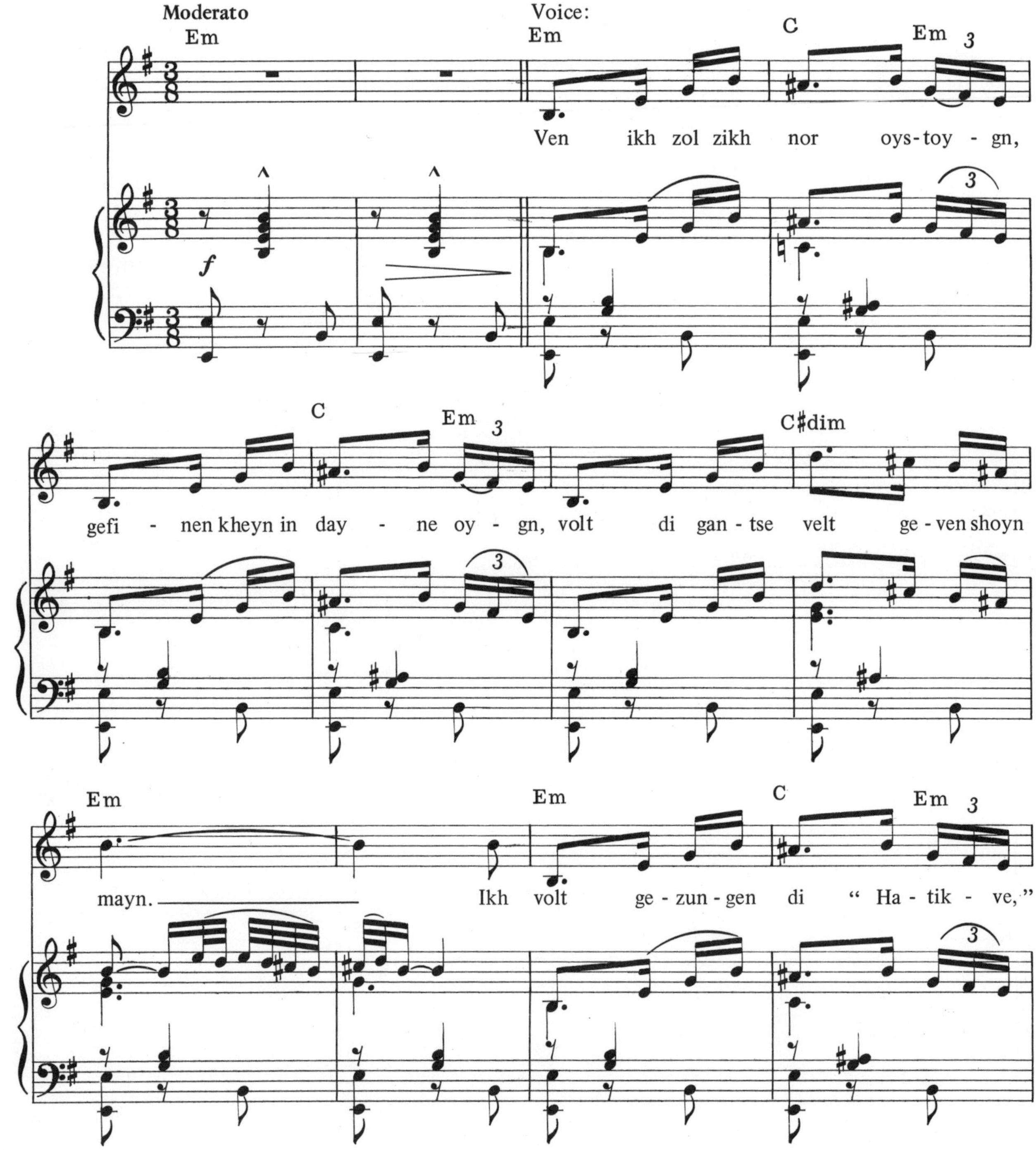

Moderato
Em
Voice:
Em C Em 3
Ven ikh zol zikh nor oys-toy - gn,
f
3
C Em 3 C#dim
gefi - nen kheyn in day - ne oy - gn, volt di gan - tse velt ge - ven shoyn
3
Em Em C Em 3
mayn. Ikh volt ge - zun - gen di " Ha - tik - ve,"
3

Em
C
3
B7
zikh ge - toy - vlt in der mik - ve, abi du zolst mit mir in ey - nem
3
Em
Am
Em
3
zayn.
Ikh volt ge-makht a ma - se-ma - tn, a
3
Am
Em
3
F♯7
knekht ge - vo - rn bay dayn ta - tn, vi Yan - kev iz bay Lo - ve - nen ge -
3

B B7 Em C Em
ven, Ikh volt ge - li - tn a - le ey - mes,
rit.
C B7 Em
un ge-mol-kn di be-hey_ mes, abi ikh zol dir shten - dik ke-nen zen.
Recit.
D♯dim Em Am6 B
Du ge - felst dokh a - ye - dn glaykh, ver es kukt nor oyf dir. Un
Recit.
D♯dim Em F♯7 B7
du host ge - fu - nen kheyn a sakh, in di oy - gn yetst bay mir.

Moderate tempo
Chorus:
Em Am6 Em Am6 Em Am6 Em B7
Zog es mir nokh a mol, oy, zog es mir nokh a mol. Vayl ikh bin
Em Am Em Eb+ D7 G6 E7
ge - rn tsu he - rn di shey - ne ver - ter fun dir.
Am Dm6 Am G#dim Am Dm6 Am E7
Zog es mir nokh a mol, oy, zog es mir nokh a mol. Vayl day-ne
Am Dm Am B7 E7
rey - dn brengt frey - dn un git mir mut on a shir. Mayn

Dm6 E Am Dm6 Am
harts, es vakst in mir a - tsin - dert fun groys freyd. Az ikh
D7 G B7
hob der - lebt tsu he - rn fun dir a - zel - khe reyd.
Em Am6 Em E7 Am Dm6 Am Am6 Em6 D♯dim
Zog es mir nokh a mol, oy, zog es mir nokh a mol, oy, n'kho-me-le, n'sho-me-le,
C♯dim B7 1. Em B7 2. Em
zog es mir nokh a mol. mol.

ZUG FARVUS?

Aaron Lebedeff sang this to Lucy Levine at the Public Theatre show which featured an array of stars and the song "A Sheyner Kholem."
Tell me why are you so dear to me?
Why is there a fire burning in my heart?
Why do I love you so?
Why do you bring paradise to my world?

Lyric by JACOB JACOBS Music by SHOLOM SECUNDA

Moderato
Intro: Em Voice: Em

Gleyb_ mir, li - ber,

Bbdim C7 Em Bbdim C7

ikh far - shtey_ dikh. Fun_ der vay - tn ven ikh_ ze_ dikh,

Em B7

heybt on mayn harts tsu kla - pn, dem o - tem ken ikh nit kha - pn, oy,

Em Am6 B Em
azh es geyt mir oys dos khayes. Her— ikh dayn ko-
B♭dim C7 Em B♭dim C7
vad - le— klin - gen, z'punkt vi a ma - lakh volt ge - zin - gen,
Em B7 Em
dir— mayn sod der - tseyl— ikh, s'vert oy - fn har - tsn frey - lekh mir.
D7 G6 Cm6 D6 G 3
Vi a le - me - le me - ket nokh ir ma - me ven zi'z
3

G6 Cm6 D6 G 3
vayt, me - ket mayn harts nokh dir_ a - zoy_ di gan - tse tsayt. Un
3
3
Gm D7 Gm Am Am6
punkt vi a kleyn ka - na - ri - kl zingt___ sheyn a shir, a -
Em Em Moderato
zoy zingt oykh mayn harts ven du bist mit mir.
Moderate tempo
Chorus: Em Em6 Em
Zog far - vos___ bist du mir a - zoy tay - er? Zog far - vos___

E B7 Em Em7
glit do in harts a fay-er? Zog far vos hob ikh dikh a-zoy lib?
(Oy,
Em6 B7 Em Em6 Em
Zog far vos kler ikh oyf mayn ge-le-ger? Zog far vos
lyu-be may-ne, du-she may-ne)
B7 Em
klapt mayn harts vi a zey-ger? Zog far vos hob ikh dikh a-zoy lib?
D A7 D7 Em D7 G Cm6
Eyn zakh ken ikh nit far-shteyn vayl s'iz mir nit a-zoy klor.
On dir bin ikh vi a blum iz on - a zu-nen-shtral.

D A7 D7 Em D Em B7
Far vos ven ikh shtey le - bn dir nemt shtay-gn mayn temp'-ra - tur?
Der-kvikst mikh punkt vi a far-shmakh - tn kvikt a va - ser - fal.
Em Em6
Zog far vos fil ikh a - zoy tsu re - dn?
Em B7
Zog far vos fil ikh dem tam gan - ey - dn? Brengst mir dem
1. Em B7 2. Em
gan - ey- dn oyf der velt. velt.

INDEX OF LYRICISTS AND COMPOSERS